Make Hay While the Sun Shines

Make Hay While the Sun Shines

Tom Pemberton

RADAR

First published in Great Britain in 2022
by Radar, an imprint of
Octopus Publishing Group Ltd
Carmelite House
50 Victoria Embankment
London EC4Y 0DZ
www.octopusbooks.co.uk

An Hachette UK Company
www.hachette.co.uk

First published in paperback in 2023

ISBN 978 1 80419 005 0

A CIP catalogue record for this book is available from the British Library.

Printed and bound in the UK

1 3 5 7 9 10 8 6 4 2

Typeset in Sabon LT Pro by Jouve (UK), Milton Keynes

This FSC® label means that materials used for
the product have been responsibly sourced.

For all the Pembertons: past, present, and future!
And for everyone who has supported me along the way

CONTENTS

INTRODUCTION

Nearly five years ago, I uploaded a one-minute video to YouTube about how to use our new raw milk vending machine at our little dairy farm on Lancashire's Fylde coast. It was all a bit rough around the edges (because my videos are obviously super polished now) and I expected about five people to watch it: the Ginger Guy with the Moustache (my dad), my mum, Joanna (now my wife!) and my sisters Penny and Amy.

I can't believe what's happened since then. As I write this, I've just passed 400,000 subscribers. And I still can't get my head around it.

I love what I do. I'm one of those people who get excited for Monday. I can't wait to go to work. I like seeing what's going to happen and how the day will go. I like hearing everyone chatting about what's gone well, what's gone wrong and what we can do to fix it. I can't hide my joy when my favourite cow is in calf for the eleventh time. I like mending things. I like getting through a list of jobs, doing them well, doing them efficiently and feeling like we're moving forwards and improving. And I love that moment of reflection on it at the end of the week, when you think about the work you've put in making the grass grow better for the cows and the knock-on effect that has on the whole farm. For me, the best thing about farming is the sense that what you sow today you'll reap later on. It's a long-term reward process.

The funny thing is I didn't always want to work on a farm. And Dad never actually made me work on the farm ever, it was always a choice. Sure, he'd take me and my sisters along with him to do little bits and bobs when we were young, and we loved having animals and tractors about. I remember that we'd feed the lambs before going to primary school each morning, which was always fun. One of my fondest memories is when Dad gave me a little pedal tractor when I was five or six. He even added a mini trailer to it. And when he chopped the grass in the summer, I used to load up my little trailer, just like him. I made a tiny little silage clamp out of red bricks to store the grass I'd collected and the Ginger Warrior made me a protective cover over it like he would do with the much bigger version. When the cows needed moving across the road, Amy, Penny and I would help Dad shepherd them along, blocking off the traffic, and we put a long line of string with rubber discs attached across any road or gateway that wasn't blocked by us. Possibly a bit dodgy on the health and safety front, but it was the 1990s.

I was in awe of how much my father did and how strong he was. I remember seeing him smack massive posts into the ground with a sledgehammer. He looked like some sort of strongman at a funfair ringing the bell at the top of the tower. And I knew how strong he was because I couldn't even get the hammer off the floor!

But it was only when I was 15 years old that I decided that farming was something I wanted to do. I remember like it was yesterday asking my dad for a boiler suit. All I wanted was a boiler suit and to start farming. And that summer, I really got my teeth stuck into it and massively enjoyed it. I realised that I like working hard and trying to better myself. I get that work ethic from my dad and he's really inspired me.

If I hadn't chosen farming, I think I would have found something else I enjoyed and would probably have applied that same work ethic I get from Dad. I used to be mad into training at the gym and I got pretty good at it. So maybe that's something I would have done professionally – gone into personal training or something like that. I think you've got to get slightly obsessed with something if you want to be really good at it.

But I'm not the brightest guy in the world – I was in learning support at school for English and was put in a class of ten instead of the usual 25–30, but I was in the top set for maths. Numbers always made sense to me – there was always one answer! I thought I was just slow, but then found out I was dyslexic around ten years old. But it doesn't have to hold you back. I had a great time at school – I got on with lots of different groups and was in the rugby team. I was sometimes the class clown and didn't take myself too seriously, as you might maybe expect from my social media stuff. One subject

I really didn't like was biology, which is funny because I've spent so much of my time studying the anatomy of animals on the farm, even down to things like how blood circulates through their bodies. But I'm a practical learner and working on the farm where I learned through example and trial and error (and there have been a fair few of the latter) taught me so much. I love biology now!

One of my favourite farming expressions is 'Make hay while the sun shines', so it seemed like the right title for this book. When things are going well and you have the opportunity to get something done, get it done! It's something my dad has passed down to me. Up on the Fylde coast, in the northwest of Lancashire, it's cold and wet a lot of the time, but what keeps me going is that I know it'll get better and when it does it's amazing up here.

I love the feeling of putting in the extra effort and time to help the cows that are struggling a bit. It's one of the most satisfying things, making a decision to, say, do everything I could to save the Charolais bullock who had broken his leg back in February 2018. Rather than put him down, which I know would have been a normal response to a serious injury like that to a farm animal, I asked the vet to splint his leg and see how he went. We gave him some TLC in the sick pens next to the parlour so I could keep an eye on him, and six weeks later he was back with the other calves, bouncing around. Yeah, it was a bit of a gamble, but he recovered, and lived a healthy happy life here, spending the summers grazing outside with the sun on his back. That's what I love – to see that animal without a care in the world and to know that he's here today because of the choice I made. So I'd do the same thing again. And I felt really supported by lots of you who sent in nice comments about that decision.

I love a bit of constructive criticism because it means I can learn how to improve things and that's why I've always asked for people to give their opinions and tell me how they do things on their farms. I feel like we're all in this together, learning from each other what's good, what's bad and how to help each other out. I'm lucky because I get very few nasty comments on the channel. And the people who just say things like, 'You're an arsehole', I can deal with fine. It's part and parcel of putting yourself out there for people to see and comment about publicly. That's not to say that the odd negative observation doesn't affect me, though, especially if it reinforces something I fear or if I'm caught at a low point. I shot a video in June 2019 about a comment I'd had on the young stock not looking healthy. It upset me a lot because I'd just had to put my dog Ben down, and I put so much effort and so many extra hours into making sure our cows were healthy and happy. My family encouraged me to focus on all the good comments, but at the time I couldn't look past it. I was in that frame of mind where I was in a bad mood so I wanted to piss myself off more, I think. My wife Jo's a really good listener, though, and made me feel better about it. And I chatted to the vet and she told me not to worry about it – she said the animals were doing really well and that's the main thing.

Now, though, a couple of years down the line, I just

ignore the negative comments. I'm confident and self-assured enough to know that I'm all right at farming. Of course I'll have moments where I think I could have done better – and I'm my own worst self-critic in that sense – but I don't react to them any more. I've got more experienced with dealing with social media and don't let it get me into a tizz. But when I started out on YouTube, things got to me a lot more. I found it all really addictive, there's no doubt about it. Getting Views and interaction makes you feel good and you just want more of it. And when a video didn't do as well as I hoped it might, I used to get nervous and think, 'God, what's happened here? The whole thing's going to come crashing down.' Part of me still feels like that and, for a while, I did get into a habit of doing things in a certain way when I uploaded videos. I can see why some sportsmen and women get superstitious about repeating things in exactly the same way to replicate a day when everything went perfectly!

I didn't believe that the things I'm fortunate enough to have achieved on YouTube could possibly happen to me. I really am just a regular guy, working hard on a farm, like so many of you. There are loads of Tom Pembertons out there! When I got 1,000 YouTube subscribers, I was amazed. I remember when I saw that 500 people had watched one of my videos, and I was stunned. Then, the idea of 10,000 subscribers was just a crazy amount and trying to reach that number felt impossible. When I actually hit 10k subscribers, it was *huge*. It sounds odd, but 10k felt more amazing at the time than 100k did, because it took so long and involved such a lot of graft to get there. Back then, I'd check the numbers loads of times a day, watching them slowly creeping up and celebrating little wins. I spent so long on my phone then, replying to everyone's comments, because it blew me away that so many people wanted to chat, encourage me or offer advice. But that's the thing I still love most about being a YouTuber: getting emails, comments, Snapchats, Instagrams, Tweets and even the odd letter (remember those?!). The effort someone's gone to to write the letter and send it to me always makes receiving letters feel like Christmas Day. And then when I learn that someone's got into farming and is learning stuff because of me, it's such an amazing feeling.

When I release a video, now, I'm usually knackered after a day on the farm and hours editing, so I just flop on the sofa at home. But I'll always deliver them and go live if I've promised to unless, for example, I'm chopping grass late. People seem to be really understanding if I'm super busy. It seems weird saying that now, when at 16 I was a lazy, lazy kid. But in farming, I found something that I loved and I realised that I enjoyed working hard. And you do work hard on a farm. We work 12-hour days, but it's more like 15 hours in the summer when we're doing field work, plus a few days when we're mowing through the night. We can't be running around 15 hours a day the whole year round, though – you just won't last. We do a 12 days on, 2 days off policy on the farm, so my days off are every other Saturday and Sunday. Although 'off' might not be quite what you think because I still feed the cows on Sunday mornings. But you get a nice few hours off if everything is going well and you've caught up on all your jobs. It's only when you talk to someone from outside agriculture that you realise that this isn't the sort of working week most folks have! But that time off is enough for me to recharge and when I come back I'm massively keen to get stuck in again.

It takes blood, sweat and tears to make a living in farming, but it's worth it. And in the process, you'll learn new things, grow as a person and see the things thrive that you've invested your time and effort into. It's massively rewarding and I honestly believe I've got the best job in the world. And I think part of that is because there so much to being a farmer. You have to be an amateur vet, midwife, carer, mechanic, handyman, tractor and telehandler driver, sheepdog, and an Olympic sprinter to chase after lambs if you leave them for too long after they've been born, to tag their ears. Sometimes things come up that I've got no idea about how to fix, but I've learned a lot from watching YouTube videos on how to do things or seeing them done in real life. I'll always ask questions and not be afraid of looking stupid, like I have done with the Wareing guys putting together the new shed (more about that in Chapter 6). And then sometimes it's just a case of good old-fashioned trial and error, like trying to fly a drone (crashing it *a lot*) and learning how to shoot and edit videos.

I'm surprised Jo puts up with it all, though, to be honest. I often ask myself, 'How can you be arsed with someone like me – farming all hours and then editing until the early morning!' And most of the time I come home, I stink of cow poo. Frankly, it's a miracle she said yes when I asked her to marry me in September 2020. Jo genuinely had no idea I was about to propose to her when I took her away that weekend to Tarn Hows in the Lake District, seven and a half years after we met at a friend's 21st birthday. And I had no idea I'd get as nervous as I did before popping the question. To be fair, though, I think I was even more nervous when I rang Jo's dad, Jon, the day before, to ask for his daughter's hand in marriage. I'm quite a traditional lad in some ways and like to do things properly. Although, I'm not sure I did it quite properly...

So I tried Jon twice on the phone and he didn't answer. Not a promising sign for a prospective son-in-law! And then half way through cobbling together some pasta for dinner (Joanna was out), the phone rang and it was Jon. *We're on*, I thought. For the life of me, I couldn't think which pub to suggest, but eventually we sorted that. I then went to the pub straight away and just about found the words to get myself a pint at the bar while I waited. I was anxious, so I didn't think to get him one, though – what a nightmare.

After chatting for a bit, I finally decided to pluck up the courage to ask the question: 'Jon – can I have your blessing to ask Joanna's hand in marriage?' (scariest moment of my life). Jon looked at me. I would say he was shocked, but seeing as I'd been sitting next to him shaking for 20 minutes, he knew exactly what was going on. He said there were three conditions to having his daughter's hand. The first: do I love her? Some questions I struggle with, like which pub to go to or which beer to choose, but I know one thing for sure: I love Joanna! The second: will I care for her through the bad times and the good? I said yes, I promise I will take good care of her and keep her safe from the cows and bees (yes, my Joanna is terrified of cows, but we'll go into that later). And the third and final condition: make sure the wedding doesn't clash with a United game! Gotta love Jon.

The engagement went without a hitch. Well, apart from me forgetting to press the 'record' button on the phone, which is especially impressive for a YouTuber. I went for the 'Shall we have a look over there?' line to distract Jo before getting on one knee. I'm just glad she looked back around! Some nice folks who could see what was happening cheered, which was lovely. The wedding was incredible, and Joanna looked amazing, although it was a bit touch and go on how many people would be able to come, given we're talking Covid-19 restrictions in 2020. In the end, we got lucky with everything easing a couple of weeks before we got married.

During the ceremony, I got my words muddled up and ending up saying, 'For better *and* worse', which got a good laugh. But that made everyone relax and the rest of it was that perfect mixture of funny and sweet. Although, for some reason the vicar didn't say, 'You may now kiss the bride.' My Joanna wasn't having that, so she asked him if she could kiss me. Love it. That's a quality wife. She knows what she wants and she gets it.

I wouldn't be where I am without Joanna by my side. And I need her there, because I'm far from perfect! When we've got a few hours off together, I'll suggest shooting a video or want to just pop back to the farm to check everything's all right instead of doing whatever it is people our age should be doing. And she'll be there, helping and supporting me. She doesn't have a background in farming, but she knows that it's hard for me to keep away from the farm when I'm so emotionally invested in it.

I love not knowing what's going to happen each day I arrive on the farm. Whether it's a happy surprise – like a new Highland calf appearing overnight or a new loaned Case arriving on the farm unexpectedly – or something difficult that comes up, I want to be there getting my hands dirty and bettering myself. I think it was a famous NFL player who once said that your fifth and final rep in the gym might be your opponent's first rep, so there's always room for improvement. Those words encourage me to keep pushing on and bettering myself even if almost all of the time I'm just competing with myself and comparing that to what I've done before. I do get competitive with my dad, though, in a sort of playful rivalry kind of way. I love guessing how many bales a field will yield and hearing Dad come up with a completely different number and the reasons for it. And I do relish the, let's face it, occasional victories.

I know I get my work ethic from my dad, who's been such a big inspiration to me. He's always going on to me about making two blades of grass grow where one is at the moment and not putting off anything till tomorrow that you can do today. Sometimes he'll say this three times in the space of a ten-minute breakfast and end with '. . . because if we don't do it, it will get on top of us.' He is always seeking to improve things where he can and that's rubbed off on me. I know he got that sense from his father, so it makes me feel in touch with the previous generations of Pembertons who worked this land. I'm proud of who we are and where we come from.

Our farm goes back six generations, back to the 1830s when the family rented a farm off the Clifton estate. It was then owned by Thomas Joseph Clifton, the head of one of the oldest and most influential families in Lancashire, and their family home was Lytham Hall, the Grade I listed Georgian mansion just over the road. My great-great-great-grandfather started farming at Birk's Farm (our farm now), around 1870. My great-great-grandfather, Thomas Pemberton (great name), took over the farm and also opened up a butcher's shop in Clifton Street in the middle of Lytham. The meat used to be delivered by butcher's bike and the milk was delivered on a horse and cart in the mornings and afternoons. Back then, it came in big churns, which the milkmen would ladle out to customers into their own jugs.

When Thomas Pemberton passed away, my grandfather John and his brother Mike bought Birk's Farm from the Clifton estate, back in 1952, with the inheritance they'd been left. From then on they worked together as J & M L Pemberton (John and Michael Leonard), which is what you'd see on the side of the horse and cart. Sadly my grandfather John passed away when I was 17 years old, but my dad talks about him often. 'He was a colossus of a fella. He was very determined, thick-skinned and hard-working, building up this farm from very little, but we had lots of jokes with him. He was a visionary, my father, and could be very single-minded. People always used to say there was three ways of doing a job: the right way, the wrong way and John Pem's way!'

John Pemberton had big plans when he inherited the farm. And the first thing he did was to sell absolutely everything, including all the shorthorn and Ayrshire cattle they owned. Then he went up to Scotland to buy cattle that were completely free of TB so he could start selling raw milk to supplement the family's income from farming. I bet people thought he was a nutter, but he wanted a clean start and saw a future in retailing the milk. So that's what he focused on, selling it from a horse and cart in glass bottles with a green top on. And to be fair to him, he was right, so props to him because he started producing raw milk on the farm, which was something that we returned to in 2016.

My dad, Andy, began farming aged just seven and started rearing cows when he was eight, although he wasn't tall enough to milk them then, even if he stood on a bucket!

He had big plans for the pocket money he earned on the farm, saving it all up to buy a second-hand car as soon as he turned 14. I'm a lot like my dad on this. The first pay cheque I ever got was from the farm when I was 19. It was just under £300 for the week, which felt like a huge amount. So I sat down and did some sums. I worked out that I could live off £120 a week easy – back then I was living with my parents in the farmhouse, so if I'm honest most of that cash went to the pub – so I set up a standing order and put £150 into another account. I've done the same thing for the last ten years, putting half of what I earn into a savings account. I remember someone telling me, when I was 14, that you could buy a house, rent it out and it would earn you more than you'd pay for the mortgage. I remember thinking, 'Why don't more people do that?' So that's exactly what I did when I was 21.

I've learned to be careful with money and we try and save it wherever we can. I know I joke a lot about one day buying a Ford Ranger, but that's still a way off. Maybe it's a dream that I'm chasing that will get replaced by another dream along the way. Whenever I think about a Ford Ranger, I think of the acceptance speech Matthew McConaughey made when he won Best Actor at the Oscars in 2014, which has left a permanent mark on me. He talked about his hero, which rather than naming someone else as you'd expect, was himself, only ten years in the future. He knows he's never going to get any closer to attaining that – his hero will always be ten years away, but it's the act of chasing that figure that keeps him hungry to keep making himself the best that he can be.

For now, though, I want to invest in the future of the farm that I'm so proud of. And with the money I've been lucky enough to earn through the YouTube success, I spend it on things that are easily as sexy as a Ford Ranger, like a new feed bin, a new slurry tanker, a new silage clamp and a massive new shed to replace some of the kit and buildings that are now a bit past it. My dad knows that each generation of Pembertons leaves its own unique stamp on the farm, as he did, and he respects, supports and embraces the changes that are happening. As he says himself, 'My thoughts aren't gospel by a long chalk. I just do what I've learned and experience tells me that we need to accept that changes are happening.'

It was Dad who nominated me for the Digital Innovator of the Year Award at the British Farming Awards without me even knowing (!), but even when we went to the award ceremony, I didn't think I'd have a chance of actually winning it. And when we got to our table, I was even more sure I wouldn't win it, because the table was right at the back of the room. So I felt comfortable having quite a few beers before it was announced.

Hearing my name called out was a massive surprise and it all seemed completely nuts. But I was so pleased to come back to the table with my family and my good friend Ross, who I met at Royal Agricultural College a good few years ago, because I never would have got to this point without my family and friends helping and believing in me.

And on that note, I want to single out my mother, Ailsa, for doing so much work that doesn't get seen. She's in charge of the bookwork, and that's a full-time job here covering everything from payroll and accounts to the mountains of other form-filling you have to do on a farm. On top of that, she handles another more-than-full-time job: looking after the Pemberton men. She's an amazing mum, an incredible cook and would do anything for any of us. My eldest sister, Amy, isn't in farming. The one that got away! She runs a dance, drama and music school in Lytham and is as dependable as she is honest and kind. Penny is my next sister and is an accountant (she's actually my accountant now – thanks, sis!). She's got a big heart and would take the clothes off her own back to keep someone else warm. Penny has three horses on the farm now, so I see a lot of her.

I'm still very much the younger brother to Penny and Amy. When we were all little, as two older sisters do, they used to dress me up as a doll for a laugh. Come to think of it, Amy still makes sure I'm looking pretty – she cuts my hair! We all get together for a Sunday roast every few weeks in the farmhouse with Mother and Father, and it's an absolute banger, full of laughter, singing and quoting movie lines.

And without all of you who watched the videos, liked them and subscribed to my channel, none of this crazy journey would be happening. I believe that social media can bring the farming community together. We get a bad rep in agriculture (or 'Ag', as we call it) for being grumpy folks and I think a lot of that is because we spend a lot of time on our own, often in remote places. But if you've got a smartphone in your pocket and you see a video of someone like you tackling the same sort of things you do with a smile on their face, even when they balls them up, it's going to make you have a laugh, feel connected and that you're part of something. It also might awaken something in you that you didn't know you had. I've met some amazing young farmers who are incredible communicators and really passionate about what they do. And we need more people like that to take the industry forward in the future.

I'm just one of these people flying the flag for Ag, showing the world what I love behind the farm gate. And that's what this book is all about. So I hope you enjoy the show!

FARM LIFE

1

EVERYDAY JOBS

The alarm on my phone wakes me up at 5.30am and I throw on some clothes and my Farm Life beanie, try not to wake Joanna and jump in the van. I park in the farm shop car park, open the gate that connects the farm to my mum and dad's house and close it again, because as I've learned the hard way, rule number one when you're working on a farm is *always* shut the gate!

I say hello to Father (aka the Ginger Guy with the Moustache, the Ginger Warrior, the Ginger Ninja or the Red Baron) in the kitchen and he'll usually come up with a motivational pearl of wisdom like 'Never put off tomorrow what you can do today.' Mind you, sometimes it'll be something like 'Thomas, that grass smells wonderful – good enough to smoke!'

I grab a cup, spoon in some coffee granules, get the trusty wellies on and wander towards the milking parlour, opening up the shed that houses our raw milk vending machine on the way. I can't walk past it without remembering that that's the place where I recorded my first YouTube video. Watching that professional, polished performance back, I just knew that the BBC would be on the phone asking me to present a show before long...

The girls (that's what I call the cows) know what time it is – grub time! – and the excitable mooing goes up a notch when they hear me turn on the milking parlour lights and switch on the parlour cleaning system. Then I head outside, open the gate and get chased by the same dozen or so keen bean cows who want to make sure I get my morning cardio fix. All of our cows tend to walk into the parlour nice and easy so we don't need to encourage them, but I tend to give them 'a hoop and a haaa' to gee them along anyway. Our milking parlour is like a lot of things on our farm: old and a bit rough around the edges, but it does the job well enough for us. I think my dad would say 'tried and tested'. It was built in 1960 and is an eight-a-side swingover system, which just means it has eight milking units and can hold eight cows in two lanes with a central gangway where the famer can walk up and down. When one lane of eight cows is done milking, you swing the units over to the other lane where the cows are waiting patiently. Each of the units has four suction cups which attach to each of the cows' teats. These connect to big glass jars suspended above which collect the milk from each cow. A friend of mine visited the farm for the first time recently and said, 'I love it – it looks like a chemistry lab inside a World War II submarine.'

If I'm honest, which I try to be, the glass jar system is a bit of a pain because it isn't as quick as other systems, which just involve one big tube which all the milk collects into. But the one joy of jars is that if you make a cock-up (and as anyone who's ever watched any of my videos will know, I'm no stranger to that) you can isolate that jar.

Before we attach the units, we use a pre-dip, a disinfectant foam that covers each teat. We leave it for 45 seconds to let it set in and soften all the muck (and there can be a bit of that sometimes), then we wipe them with paper towels to get the girls nice and clean. Then I start the machine to activate the suction pump on the milking units, and then attach a cup to each teat. When the cow's finished milking, the units detach automatically and swing back to the central gangway. So you need to keep your wits about you lest you get walloped across the face by a swinging unit (it still happens to me surprisingly often). If one of the cups loses suction, it makes a hissing sound, so you know there's a problem.

Once the first eight are in and milking, then comes the most important moment of any farmer's morning: the brew. I fill up my coffee cup with hot water and select which cow's gonna be kind enough top it up with milk for me to make what I like to call a farmer's cappuccino. Cow selection is key to any good brew. We have lots of different breeds of cow on the farm and they each have their own special qualities, but I'm after some properly creamy milk, so I go for the brown or red cows (Brown Swiss or Ayrshire). I challenge you to make a better brew than I do at 6.30 in the morning! The only trouble is I tend to leave my mug in a different place on the farm each time and find it two weeks later.

I love morning milking because it's quiet, it's time by yourself where you can think about everything that needs doing in the day or stick your headphones in and listen to a podcast. Also, you get to see all of your milking cows, so you can notice anything unusual. You get to know your cows really well, what they do and why they normally do it. I can recognise most of them from just their back ends now! They've all got unique personalities. Some are cheeky little minxes, like number 253, who without fail starts nibbling bits of milking equipment every morning. Or she'll pull the paper towel out from the dispenser and scatter it all over the floor. I wouldn't change this sort of thing for the world, though, and it makes me smile more than it occasionally drives me nuts.

After the first eight are done milking, I spray each of their teats with an iodine solution to disinfect and protect them from mastitis (which can be really nasty) and let them out before washing down the floor and unhooking the chain and allowing the next eight in. All in all, it takes about two and a half hours to milk all the cows. But hopefully, that's going to come down in a big way because the next big project on the farm (well, after the others we've got going on) is to build a new parlour. And with a new parlour, we could get milking times down from two and a half hours to say one and a half hours, which, when milking twice a day would make an unbelievable difference on our little farm. This might not seem a lot to everyone at home – two hours a day – but that adds up to 730 hours a year! Working my usual 70-hour week, I will have gained over ten weeks *each year*! For any business, that sort of time saving is amazing, but on a farm when time is already short, it's incredible. The only minor issue is the fact that you won't get much change out of a quarter of million pounds for a new parlour. And then there's the headache over whether you're going to make enough money to pay off the interest and the debt. Investment on a farm is always a balancing act!

The other major plus to quicker milking times and less time spent in the parlour is more time with my family, more time by myself and more time with my wife (it feels good to be able to say that now!). I would like to have kids one day and, if, on Christmas morning, I can have my cows milked, cleaned, fed and bedded up before the kids get up, I will be a very happy man.

Each cow has coloured bands on its tail which tells me the amount of feed to give them while they're being milked – I tap in the amount to a little screen and the feed comes through a dispenser in front of each cow. The feed, or cake, is full of energy, protein, vitamins and minerals and they love it! A green band on the tail means 3lb of cake, a blue band 4lb and a yellow one 5lb (that's between about 1.3kg and 2kg). Our standard amount for the dairy cows is 8lb (3.6kg), so most of our cows have one yellow and one green band on their tails. A lot of farms have auto-ID systems where you've got a barcode attached to the cow's ear, so the scanner reads it and automatically dispenses the right amount of food. Clever stuff. We use what my dad calls an Tom-o-matic system, which works for us – well, most of the time, anyway. The cows who aren't producing much milk don't need as much feed. If we did feed them as much as the higher milk-yielding cows, they'd get quite chunky, which can cause all sorts of health issues. Any cows who are a bit under the weather and are being treated for it have three red bands on their tails to make it easy to spot them. I attach a separate milking unit to them and the milk gets dumped so we don't end up with any antibiotics or medicines in the main milk tank. I'm really proud of how clean our milk is here at Pembertons. The year we started producing raw milk (milk straight from the cow), we won an award for its quality.

At our farm, we've got Ayrshires (the mainly red ones), Friesians (the mainly black ones), and Brown Swiss crosses. Some of our dairy cows have got a bit of Holstein in them (the classic black and white patterned ones), but we're trying to stop any more Holstein crosses because we find that they're not as good on their feet and aren't as good at grazing. Yes, Holsteins and Holstein crosses produce the most milk, but that's not as important to us here as making sure the product is the best it can be for our customers. The Brown Swiss is just a bigger version of a Jersey cow, really. They look beautiful, are really friendly and are great grass grazers (try and say that quickly); the only problem is they sometimes can be a bit of a pain in the arse to milk.

We milk what we call the 'Highs' first. 'Highs' means 'high-yielding cows' – the cows that produce the most milk. These cows have recently had calves, so their milk production is really high (it reaches a peak around 80 days after calving). And to keep up the amount the Highs are producing, they need lots of energy, so they get more feed when they're being milked. The next group of cows are the 'Lows' – the low yielders. The low yielders are pregnant (what we call 'in calf'), so they're not producing as much milk because they're using their energy to grow a calf. The third group are the 'Dries'. These are the girls who are about two months away from calving – they get some TLC during this time, chill out and have a bit of a rest in a separate field. They need to prepare for giving birth and while they're in this phase we don't milk them, which explains why they're called dry cows.

Seven times a week after milking, we funnel the girls through the Hoofcount footbath we had installed recently to replace our knackered one. I got ridiculously excited about this bit of kit – it's like the Rolls-Royce of footbaths! – and not even a cold, windy, very wet February morning was going to stop the massive smile on my face. Father and I had both put a lot of research into buying one and spoke to loads of farmers and hoof trimmers about it, including friend of the farm Graham (the Hoof GP), who bloody loves them. Our foot trimmer, Ross Anthony, said he'd seen one at another farm and the difference it made was night and day. And the final word from Father on the matter: 'If you're going to have a footbath, you may as well have the best.' Weird to have a brand new, shiny bit of kit on our farm, though!

The footbath automatically flushes away what's in it and refills it after 75 cows have been through it, so each cow is getting the same treatment. That's one massive improvement over our old one, because we were never sure whether the cows at the end of the queue were getting any benefit from it, after loads of other girls had been through it, with some peeing and pooing when they stood still in the water. The new one's also got a soft rubber floor, so it's comfortable for the girls under hoof. The footbath is connected to two sets of chemicals, which protect against different foot problems a cow can get, and is clever enough to automatically change the type of chemical solution each time we use it. So I don't need to handle the chemicals any more, which is a bonus given that they're carcinogenic! And on top of everything, the machine even cleans itself.

Sorry, I'm a bit sad and I'm getting well excited about all these features! But this bit of kit improves so many things for us. Foot health is so important for cows and we really care about our animals here. If cows have bad feet, they're less likely to get up and eat and generally move about. If they eat less, they'll have less condition, so they'll get thin and will have less energy to produce more milk, less energy to get in calf and they generally won't be as happy. Plus, it helps to protect against digital dermatitis, which causes painful lesions on their feet.

This sort of small improvement taps into an idea that's a really big deal for me here on the farm: marginal gains. This was a concept that Dave Brailsford, the former performance director of British Cycling, came up with soon after he took the role in 2003. He believed that if you broke down everything that went into riding a bike and then improved each thing by 1 per cent, you'd end up with big cumulative gains. This approach transformed the British Cycling team's success on the track and played a huge part in Britain's total of 16 cycling golds at Beijing 2008 and London 2012 and their dominance of the Tour de France from 2012. It's something that's really inspired me and I'm always thinking about it!

For example, lameness in cows is proven to reduce their chances of calving by 25 per cent, because lame cows are less likely to exhibit heat – the only fertile part of their reproductive cycle. So if you improve the condition of their feet even just a little bit, say with a new footbath, your cows will have more calves and produce more milk. A small improvement at one stage can lead to a huge impact elsewhere.

I apply this kind of approach to my work every day and believe that if you put in an extra 2 per cent of effort, your herd productivity could increase by 10 per cent. I try and gear everything towards making sure tomorrow is better, and with livestock you're always thinking a couple of years ahead. When I 'serve' a cow (farmer speak for artificially inseminate, which is how we get our dairy cows in calf, but more on that later), it will take at least two years for that calf to start producing milk. So the things I'm reaping now are dividends from a couple of years ago. It's all part of the 'If you save up now, it'll be worth it later on' mentality that I've grown up with and that I can give the Ginger Warrior a lot of credit for.

Some people tell me that I should do the living now and I get that, but life is long (you hope) and you've got to plan for it. I know a lot of farmers who have ended up with injuries after years of hard labour on the farm. My dad struggles with back and knee problems, partly because he used a tractor with a very heavy clutch to buck-rake (a long-toothed rake attachment that you use to transport and compress grass). Plus, he was using a buck-rake that was facing backwards back then. Nowadays it's all flappy paddles that make you feel a bit like you're in a sports car, and that's fun, but it also means that I'm not moving myself that much at all. The amount of strain you used to have to put your body through on a farm is just crazy. That being said, there are some things I do that I probably shouldn't. On a farm, you're always lifting things. I'm young and I want to save time here and there, so I'll chuck two sacks of whatever I'm carrying on my back, no bother. But the amount of power it takes to lug 50kg (110lb) onto your back is a lot. I'm lucky because I did a lot of weight training when I was younger and learned how to lift things properly, using my legs, but I know it's going to have an effect over time. So I've been wondering about implementing something that my friend the Red Shepherdess (Hannah Jackson) told me.

She came across a shepherd in Australia on a farm with 18,000 sheep and 18 dogs working in packs of six. The dogs would work for a day and have two days off. After six years they were knackered, absolutely done. So the shepherd started getting the dogs massaged one day a month and he managed to get another four years out of them. Physio for dogs! So I started thinking: why don't we as farmers do that for ourselves, the last weekend of every month, get a sports massage and look after ourselves? I think we need to try and battle through the attitude of 'It'll be all right until it's not all right', something that I'm guilty of.

Although I haven't started to make any changes to my routine just yet, these are the sort of things that I think about – how to make small long-term changes for the better – when I've got time to myself milking the cows.

And when the girls are all done milking, I hose down the parlour, wash the milking units and then set the system to begin its cleaning cycle so we're all ready to crack on for the afternoon milking. We milk the girls twice a day, and all in all we end up with about 3,000 litres of milk a day, which works out at around 1 million litres a year. While the cleaning cycle's on, I'll use the time to check the calving boxes right next to the parlour which is where the newborns and ones that aren't looking 100 per cent live for a bit on straw bedding. That way, we can keep a close eye on anything that needs a little bit more attention. So I get them all some feed, bed the pens up and by the time I've done that the cleaning cycle should have finished. By then, it's about 8.30 and it's time for a hearty, well-earned breakfast in the farmhouse kitchen, which Mum cooks. Dad and I are lucky boys. It's a good chance to have a catch-up with Dad, but me and Father (or *Father and I*, as he corrects me in every video – you'd think I would have learned that by now!) have usually had a quick chat somewhere along the way before that about what we're doing today. Normally this is the same thing he's told me once at 6am in the house, then at 7 when he pops his head into the parlour and then again at breakfast. It's good because if I wasn't listening the first time I know I will have two more chances to take it in!

Things happen a bit differently during the winter months (and by that I mean about October to mid-April when we let them out), when all the girls are inside in their sheds. If I've got a milker in looking after the girls, which is happening more and more these days, I'll start my morning at 6am scraping up the back shed, beginning with the squeegee in the corners to make life easier for myself before I jump on the scraper tractor. And if it's raining, well, look on the bright side – it makes scraping easier! Although, having said that, it does mean you're sitting on a tractor with a wet arse. Hey ho.

Tom's Top Tip
When mucking out larger pens, always start at the corners and sides – the tractor can do the rest!

Like any tractor driver, the more I don't have to get off the tractor, the better. Our scraper tractor, an International B275, has only been with us for five years, but it's older than my dad! It was built in 1958, has an eight-speed gearbox and chugs out a tidy 38hp (although it may have lost a couple of horses over the years). It has a bog-standard scraper attachment on the back which gets used and abused, like every scraper on every farm. I also use it for rounding up cows and Dad loves it for rolling silage in the barn in summer. Silage is grass (or another crop) that has been chopped, densely packed and covered with sheeting in the storage clamp to remove the air. Left there, it soon starts to ferment, which preserves as much of its original goodness as possible. We use the scraper tractor every day and that's why it's probably the most important tractor on the farm. It looks like the little red tractor toy you used to have as a kid, too – it's a classic! Although, mind you, it's had a few knocks over the years and some of them weren't even my fault. A cow bashed the front end, which gives it what I like to call an 'aerodynamic' dent, and it sticks out a tad more than the wheels in certain areas, but the brakes still work and it's perfect for getting in and out of our buildings. The only negatives are that sometimes the cows lick the battery isolator, which kills the engine, and you can't see the radiator without taking the bonnet off. Oh, and there's no cab, but as my dad says, 'If it's raining, put a coat on!'

So I scrape the muck into the slats in the yard that lead to the slurry lagoon. I wish we had slats closer to the shed so the area in front of it didn't end up such a mess, but we're not going to have that problem with the new shed. Winning!

Then I fill up the wheelbarrow with sawdust and bed the cows in the back shed up. I do this by picking up a shovelful of sawdust and jiggling it left and right as I sidestep along the beds. It works a charm, the sawdust shake!

I also make sure the Highs have got fresh feed in the troughs for after they've finished milking. We add a bag of meal on top, which encourages them to eat up their leftover food, and we can put the new stuff on top. That way, when they walk back to their shed, they'll go straight to the food and eat while standing up (rather than sitting down first), which keeps their teats clean and infection down. We're definitely going to do this in the new shed.

Wisdom from the Ginger Warrior
It's a bit like putting salt and vinegar on your chips to make you eat the last chips before you get a new lot of chips on top of the soggy ones on the bottom. It's spicing up what's there to get the maximum amount eaten and the minimum wasted. Waste is cost!

If the troughs are empty, I'll put in 450kg a side in the morning and around 650kg in the evening, but there's usually a bit left in them, so I dump a couple of hundred kilograms using the trusty Manitou telehandler – the workhorse of the farm. For those of who you haven't seen one, it's a bit like a super-powerful forklift/crane hybrid, with a telescopic arm that can extend upwards and forwards. You can fit it with lots of different attachments according to the job you've got on. Like most of our equipment, it's seen a few summers and winters, but it can lift 2.3 tonnes and does everything you tell it to. Needs a bit of a wash, though.

I'll rave about our Manitou until I'm blue in the face mainly because before it arrived on the farm, we had to rely on a two-wheel-drive 885 loader tractor. WHAT. A. NIGHTMARE (despite what the Warrior says). Now, I don't want to sound ungrateful, and I know a loader tractor is better than using a pitchfork, but everything takes too long, the turning circle is rubbish and because it's only two-wheel drive, all the weight is on the front so it goes through wheel bearings for fun! I'm all about efficiency and our Manitou has certainly improved that, halving loading times for some jobs. So when we got it, it felt like someone had invented the wheel!

Then it's on to the calf shed, which is where the calves live that are between three and eight weeks old. This is one of my favourite jobs because they're beautiful, friendly and very playful creatures. They start off in single pens and then move on to doubles when they're a bit older. Well, that's the plan in theory, anyway. A lot of the time, the cheeky calves have decided to play musical pens and jump into each other's enclosures during the night. To be honest, I always quite enjoy that and switching them all back.

First, I empty their water buckets, then we feed them half a bucket of nice warm fresh milk each (it comes straight from the parlour), which works out as about 2.5–3 litres (½–⅔ gallon). I don't know why, but I like to keep the Charolais and Angus calves (the beefers) in one group and the dairy cows in another, but it wouldn't matter either way because they all get exactly the same treatment and feed at this point in their lives. When you feed calves, it's the perfect time to check if they're all nice and healthy. You can usually tell if they're all right because their heads are completely invisible, properly in the bucket gobbling up the milk. Next I refill the water buckets, give them some cake, bed them up with some straw and make sure they've all got a bit of hay in the corner of their pens to give them a bit of roughage in their bellies. Last job here is to feed the two goats which we've got in here at the moment. We feed them in two different bowls now because Lottie is a bit of a bully and doesn't let Nancy anywhere near the grub. We come in and check the calf shed three or four times a day to make sure they're doing all right – eating, drinking, growing and generally messing about.

Then I used to move on to the Lows building where I do the same *scraping up and bedding up* routine. You know how sad I am? I know that it takes exactly eight scrapes in the scraper tractor to do this whole shed. Then I grab the squeegee just to give it a final tidy. The next thing is to grab some bags of cake and put it in the trough in the Lows building.

I say 'used to' above because by the time you're reading this we'll have our brand new shed here to replace the Lows building! The old building had served us well for 50+ years, but it was getting a bit tired. Well, the stalls were bending, some had fallen off, the beds were all different sizes and shapes and the feed troughs were way too small. And there were more than a few holes in the roof, despite what Dad would say about them 'encouraging airflow'. It's had a good life, but we figured that rather than getting a new roof and keep fixing things that weren't working for some time, we would do it all at once, knock it down and rebuild. The cost of it all still hurts me! But I think it needed doing. It's going to save so much time because I'll just be scraping one shed out instead of two and I'll be able to do all the beds at once. I won't be scraping muck through the yard, either, so it's going to be cleaner, too.

This adventure with the new shed feels like the first proper new footprint I'm making on the farm. As Dad always tells me, 'Each generation leaves its stamp on the farm', and I guess this is mine. Yeah, I've invested in some new equipment already, like the feeding tower we put in in 2020, but this is a massive project. And it's scared the life out of me, to be honest, overseeing such a big undertaking. But we're in good hands with Wareing, the construction company from Wrea Green – just up the road from us. Wareing and Pembertons have been working together since 1936, when my grandfather Thomas Pemberton asked them to re-roof an old chicken shed for £12. Couldn't buy a small sheet of corrugated roofing for that now! Myself and Chris Wareing are the fourth generation of this partnership and not many businesses can say that. And the Wareing team have done a cracking job on the new shed and have coped with me messing about with drones, filming everything and borrowing their equipment to set up time-lapse cameras. But you've got to give the YouTube public what they want!

The next job is to feed the calves in the calf pens next to the parlour – this is where we put the newborn calves and any sick animals, because it's right in the middle of the farm and we can check up on them all the time. We stick a bit of straw or sawdust in there, depending on how chilly it is outside. While I'm moving from place to place around the farm, I'll be checking over gates, making sure the girls (and boys) are all right. Happy livestock, happy farmer!

Then it's on to feed the guys with big horns – the Highlands – in the fields in front of the viewing area. I probably check these guys five or six times every morning, just because they're really cool and the novelty of having such amazing-looking animals on the farm hasn't worn off yet after nearly six years. A lot of people still message me to ask why we've got Highlands on the farm. Well, here's the answer, straight from the Ginger Guy with the Moustache:

I always wanted something a bit quirky and a bit different and I was after something for people to come and see. I always liked Highland cows. There used to be Highland cows on the land we rent over the road and it created a lot of interest. The coach tours from Blackpool back in the day used to come past the famous Highland cows of Ballam Road. Plus, I like the look of them, they live outside and look after themselves, although they can be a bit awkward to handle (they've got bloody big horns, don't you know!).

The first I heard of it, Dad was coming back from hospital for a check-up after his knee operation six years ago and told me he was off to have a look at some Highlands. I knew he wasn't just having a look. When Dad says he's 'having a look', it means he's been thinking about this for a while and he's already bought it in his mind. So, two days later, a trailer turned up with two Highland cows aboard. And then Dad came over rubbing his hands. 'Look at them, eh! I figured we couldn't keep waiting and hanging about. So you make a decision, and get on with it.' Fair enough, Father.

Next, I jump in the tractor that I've already connected to the mixer feeder (which mixes up the different components of the cows' feed and dispenses it) and fill it up with the feed for our cows. It's a combination of meal, Selco (specialised feed that's high in protein and energy) and silage from our farm. Now it may not surprise you to learn that the gauge is broken on the mixer feeder, but I can tell from the way it rumbles roughly how many grabs I've put in or if it's spilling over the top. I know that's not a great solution, but you get used to your kit and how your kit should sound – we work with what we've got! I'll use the mixer feeder to feed the cows here and the ones in the sheds we rent over the road. Sometimes if I'm starving, I'll make a quick diversion to the kitchen for a cheeky bacon butty on my way over the road, but normally I just push on through. It can take a little while pulling out onto Ballam Road, the main road that sits next to our farm, but most of the time some nice folks let me out. I always thank the people who are waiting politely behind the tractor while I'm using it on the road. It doesn't hurt to say thank you, does it?

After I've finished over the road, I come back and feed the dry cows back here. And then I'm done for the morning. We've milked about 115 cows this morning, fed about 340 animals and we've cleaned everywhere out. Job's a good 'un!

In the summer, everything's a bit easier because all the girls are outside happily munching on grass. But there are always a couple of rules I follow when I'm outside with them. The first is to give them plenty of distance – about 1.5m or so – particularly the older girls who are a bit slower. I don't make the cows run, either – they don't need to. Of course, some of the younger ones run and bounce around because they're excited – that's fine and it's one of the best feelings you get as a dairy farmer!

Sometimes I don't need to round them up for morning milking – they're already waiting patiently by the gate. But if they're a bit reluctant or there are a few stragglers (there's always one, isn't there!), I start up the trusty scraper tractor (minus the scraper), open the gate to their field and do my best sheepdog impression, slowly encouraging them towards the parlour. Then I shut the gate and we're off.

Next I head out the entrance to the farm shop and right across Ballam Road into one of the fields we rent. The cows come and say hello to me at the gate, which is always nice. If any of them don't, I don't take it personally, but it does mean there's a fair chance that they have a health issue that I'll need to check out. We give the young stock, bulling heifers and our bull, Neptune, some cake every day: we announce this with a bit of bag rustling, which usually makes them trot over. It's a great management tool to keep them friendly, which helps us out massively when we need to move them (or if we've got an escapee situation, which does happen over the summer months), which we do every day in the summer – for the dairy cows, anyway. We want the girls to be on a different pasture in the morning and night, so they're always on the nice lush grass that makes that top-quality Pem's milk!

Next I head back to the farm and jump in the Kawasaki golf cart that Dad bought from the local driving range, complete with all-over grille to protect you from the odd misdirected golf ball. Yes, the door swings open and shut at will and you freeze your arse off in winter, but that's all part of the charm. The Kawasaki takes me further down Ballam Road and into the entrance to the other fields we rent a little further along. We'll feed all the cows a bit of cake, although the dries only get about a quarter the amount that we give the others. That's just because they don't need the extra energy to produce milk. I'm also giving them a fly lick, which both keeps the flies away and provides a mineral boost, which is bang on because they'll be calving soon.

Wisdom from the Ginger Warrior

'If you can't drive the best vehicle in the world, drive the worst in the world. You're equally well noticed either way!'

Then we come on to everyone's least favourite job on the farm: mucking out, but it warms you up, keeps you fit and doesn't half wake you up in the morning. So, grab your trusty fork. First rule of forking? Don't try and be a hero and lift too much. Get the top off and work in layers (think onions – or ogres, if you're a *Shrek* fan). That way you can get through it so much better without knackering yourself out. After the fork's gone as far as it can, we brush out the rest, which needs a bit of elbow grease. Then we sprinkle a bit of lime on the floor to help absorb moisture and keep the infection down before bedding down with straw. I know it's never going to be perfect, but we do our best with what we've got, and if you keep the beds clean and tidy, it helps to keep the calves nice and dry and healthy (it's all about the marginal gains, remember!). In the bigger pens, I clean out the front bit, where their feed troughs are, all the time. That way, they go back to their beds at the back of the pens with dry feet, so their beds are cleaner. But when it's all looking a bit gross, we fire up the Manitou, fix the bucket attachment if it's not already on and then boom, boom, boom, chuck the muck into the midden (the waste dump, although it doesn't really go to waste – we'll use it to help fertilise the fields). Then we bed up again. I really like this kind of job – it's a very satisfying feeling that you're cleaning out the old muck and getting everything fresh again, especially when they start bouncing around in the new stuff.

At about 1pm, I hoover up a chicken wrap from the farm shop, reply to messages on my phone and usually catch up on a bit of paperwork in the office that needs doing. Stuff like recording how much milk's gone into the main tank in the morning and registering new births. Everything born on the farm has to get a passport, and we need to register each animal in order to apply for a passport. And put two tags in their ears as well.

Then, before I know it, it's time to feed and water the calves, bring the cows in again and get ready for afternoon milking. In the summer, I usually turn the big fans on in the parlour to cool the cows down and to keep the flies off their backs. The cows are the most important thing on our dairy farm. We have to make sure, from the day-olds to the ten-year-olds, that they are the healthiest they can be. Having 16 big cows (and a fairly big Tom) in a small parlour does crank up the heat a good few degrees over the outside temperature, but on a plus note, it makes it warmer in winter. Always look on the bright side!

2

NOW AND THEN JOBS

There are lots of jobs around the farm that happen as and when, whether it's an occasional milk round, repairing fences or freeing a Highland cow who's managed to get her head stuck in a gate. Then there are the dirty jobs that I always seem to end up doing (it's all part and parcel of being the farmer's son), like unblocking drains and fishing things out of the slurry lagoon.

I still help out with the odd morning milk round on Sundays (as does Dad). Some of the customers are convenience stores, who take bottles, and others are cafes and restaurants, who tend to want pergals – the big 13.5-litre (3-gallon) tubs of milk that go into a frothing machine or a dispenser so they don't keep having to muck about changing bottles over. It's great to keep up that personal connection with the customer, and it only takes an hour or so. And to be honest, after a heavy week on the farm, I'd rather be moving a milk bottle from A to B than a bull.

Fortunately, I haven't had any 'near misses' with one of our bulls, but Dad has. Maybe they just don't like gingers!

MST (Moss Side Tom), a Holstein bull we had a few years ago, got behind Dad and flicked him up into the air, leaving him in a heap on the floor. The first I heard of it was at breakfast just afterwards. Dad looked up from his newspaper and casually told me and Ross (the good mate of mine I mentioned earlier, who was staying with us) that he'd just been upended by the bull and that his glasses and phone had fallen out of his pocket. 'But it's all right – I know exactly where they are!' he said, looking up and smiling. Classic Father. Mum completely freaked out. So I got up and rang Dad's phone: to his credit, he was bang on about where it was in the field.

Then, a couple of years later, Lloyd, an Ayrshire bull we'd had on the farm for about eight months, nuzzled Dad in a holding area and managed to knock him into a feed trough. Fortunately, Dad was OK, not that he'd tell us even if he wasn't. He's not one to make a fuss, as I think you can tell by now. Sometimes a bull can just be a bit of a nob, and I'm afraid Lloyd was one of them. We all know someone like Lloyd, which is why we moved him on after eight months. But most of the bulls we've had here on the farm we've loved. A few years back, when we had to let Toby go, it was one of the saddest days I've had on the farm. He'd been a great lad, with us for three and a half years and loved a comb and a scratch (and a cheeky bit of white bread), but his heifers had now come into the milking herd, so he'd basically got no more cows to serve. I thought about not uploading the video of him going, but I want to show everything that goes on here: good, bad and, in this case, sad.

And then just a few months ago, Mr Neptune, our Angus bull and a friendly giant who'd been with us nearly four years, went lame with something that seemed quite serious. It was a massive blow. Not least because everyone loves Neptune here, he's got a really good temperament, never causes any aggro and his calves are fantastic. He'd gone lame before, both on and off camera, but this time it was on his front foot and it happened very quickly. He spent most of the day I shot the video barely moving and not wanting to put any weight on the foot. When I had a good look at him in the field, it seemed like he might have done something to his shoulder, and that's when I started to get quite worried. Eventually, he lay down on the grass and the following morning I found him in exactly the same position, which is a really bad sign. Dad and I got him into the trailer and took him back to the farm, but the poor guy needed looking at ASAP. I got a block on his foot to see if that would help but it didn't and it became clearer that it was his shoulder that was causing the problem and that he'd probably fallen on it.

Despite not moving very much at all since we brought him back to the farm, he was still a hero, even trying to serve some cows on three legs, but you could tell he wasn't in a good way. Unfortunately, with the front feet on such heavy animals, you can't really do much to cure them. We got lucky on a bullock with a broken front foot that Andy the vet put a cast on some years back, and he recovered really well, but he was a fraction of the weight of Mr Nep. It's just one of those freak accidents that happen and you can't do anything about. So we had to take the very sad decision for Neptune to leave the farm. I fed him some hay, gave him some cake, made him as comfortable as I could and gave him lots of attention, but when you know, you know and you don't want to see an animal suffer. It was a really difficult video to film, but I want people to know that it's not always rainbows and sunshine here. And you've got to have the bad days to have the good ones. I knew that he'd had about as good a life as you can, with fresh grass, room to roam, a cow brush both inside and out and, to top it off, a new set of ladies every six to eight weeks. He'd been an absolute legend and he would be missed.

No matter how calm a bull might seem, you have to take certain precautions when you try and move them. Although, sometimes I wish I could just say, 'Lad, you're on your way to a field with a hundred cows in it – you're gonna have the time of your life, so cheer up!'

The first thing to remember about bulls is not to get too close unless you have to, because, well, you really don't want to piss off an animal with horns who weighs as much as a small car in his flight zone – an area 6 metres or so around him. The second thing: be calm, assertive and don't turn your back on him. And the third is, if you're moving him through a narrow area, know exactly where your exit points are before you start and make sure you can hurdle a fence if you need to.

Tom's Top Tip
Always move a bull together with a heifer if you can – then you'll find he doesn't mind being moved around!

Probably the only thing that Mr Neptune wasn't that great at was personal grooming. And specifically, he didn't move his tail when he pooed. Maybe that's just what happens when you don't have any competition for the females on the farm – you get a bit lazy. So, every so often I had to trim his tail with the clippers to make him look more presentable. You have to get quite good at rear-end barbering as a farmer. We clip the cows' tails about four times a year to make sure the 'bag area' (the udders) is as clean as possible. The clippers are a pretty clever gadget and don't ever nick the tail, only remove the hair. On the plus side, it means that you, the farmer, don't get whacked about the face by a hairy, poo-covered swinging tail, although, having said that, you do get whacked round the face with the end of a freshly trimmed tail, and Holy Moly, that doesn't half sting. Swings and roundabouts!

While we're clipping the cows' tails we also trim their back ends a bit, especially if they've started getting 'muck buttons' (clumps – lovely) which aren't washing away in the rain. A mucky back end tends to spread muck about and increases the chances that flies will decide to move in. And believe me, you don't what that happening, because it leads to one of the grossest things you can come across as a dairy farmer. Maggots. Yuck.

Hoof trimming is another one of those things you'll end up doing as a dairy farmer if you notice an overgrown claw or spot that they're not moving as you'd like. Ross Anthony is our foot trimmer who makes the short trip from Preston to check as many of the cows as he can, or will have a look if one of the girls or boys have gone lame and I can't solve the problem. Also, my friend Graham Parker, the Hoof GP, heads down to the farm once in a while. But I'll always try and fix an issue myself if I can and I'm proud of the fact that whenever Graham comes along for a check-up, very few of the cows need any real treatment.

The trouble is that cows aren't really designed to step on concrete and most of the floors on the farm are, you've guessed it, concrete. Annoyingly, concrete can cause some parts of the hoof – the sole and wall (the front of the hoof) – to grow more than usual. If it's allowed to get worse and worse, they'll struggle to bear their own weight evenly (which is a lot, around 150kg (330lb) on each foot, which, just for reference, is about 30kg (66lb) more than the weight of Dwayne 'The Rock' Johnson). After a while, this can make them lame. So, if I notice an overgrown toe or parts that look like they're wearing unevenly, I'll manoeuvre them into the cow crush and get to work with the grinder or the hoof knives to even them out and get them more comfortable.

First of all, we secure the cow in the cow crush (basically a strong cage that safely immobilises them), so we can elevate whichever leg needs to be looked at. I've found that a cow crush is one of those things that is better when it's a bit mucky because the cows kind of know it's normal and go in it a bit easier. When it's super clean, they tend to be suspicious and it can be more of a struggle! The same thing happens in a nice shiny trailer when you're trying to move cows – they prefer a bit of muck and sawdust! When it's winter time and generally a bit wet underfoot (well, underhoof), I usually put a bit of sawdust down beneath the crush so their feet can get a bit of traction, which helps them load much better.

First we funnel them into the crush, usually encouraging them into the channel running along back of the stalls in the shed next to the parlour. It's really important to keep them as chilled out as possible once they're in the crush so we don't cause them any stress and can get them out as soon as we can. The front feet are the hardest to do if you don't have a tipping crush – a clever bit of kit that picks up the cow and tips it onto its side using hydraulics. It may not be a surprise to learn that we don't have one of those here, though! So it can occasionally be a two-man job getting the cow's front foot in position, but sometimes I can do it by myself. I always wear gloves and an apron for this job, and just to reassure you, I have done a three-day course on the Dutch five-step method of foot trimming, so I do half-know what I'm doing – I'm not just giving it a go!

I use the angle grinder to begin with, fitted with special discs that trim hoofs. You've got to be careful with this one, because if you're not you can take more off than you need to and that'll lead to a red-faced Ginger Warrior. Then I use the hoof knives (there's one for the left hoof and one for the right, with blades that match the contours of the hoof) to trim any loose and dried-out bits of horn. The Hoof GP even gave me some magnetic ones that stick to the cow crush – what a guy!

Wisdom from the Ginger Warrior

'You can always take a little bit more off, but take too much off and you'll struggle to glue it back on!'

The Highlands are a little trickier so, nice guy that I am, I usually bring the cow crush to them in the field using the Manitou. Trying to get the Highlands to do something unfamiliar can range from surprisingly easy to a complete nightmare where an escapee cow runs down the middle of Ballam Road – I'm looking at you, Meghan! Luckily, my brother-in-law is fast as lightning, and a very nice man in a white van used his vehicle to block the traffic, so no harm was done, except maybe to my heart rate.

Trimming Cardhu the Highland bull (and in case you're wondering, yes, the bulls that come to us from Robert and Wendy in Hellifield are all named after whiskies) didn't quite go to plan. The first problem was that his massive head with the big old horns wouldn't fit through our crush, so I had to improvise using a halter around his head. And his back end was small compared to the dairy cows, so it slipped under the chain that's supposed to hold them at the back. Thankfully he didn't seem to notice. And then the Highland girls, Minnie and Harriet, started nibbling my tool box in protest. It wasn't going so well! But we got the job done, spraying a cut on the inside of his back foot with disinfectant and copper sulphate and applying a bandage. I usually go for a pink bandage because you can see it a mile away if it comes off. This helps to make sure it doesn't get missed and end up getting into the slurry pumps or the slurry spreader, because that, my friends, is an absolute nightmare of a job. In fact, 'Why isn't the slurry pump working?' is probably the biggest can of worms a farmer can face.

Slurry is all the animal muck and water run-off from washing out the parlour that we direct into the drainage slats in the yard using the scraper tractor. As the Warrior says, 'It's all part of the cycle of dairy farming – feed, poo, recycle, feed, poo, recycle. We've got 300 head of cattle on this farm, so we're never short of muck. I mean, it's muck, muck, muck!' Thankfully, it makes a great fertiliser, so we spread it on the fields in the warmer months to help the grass grow thick and strong. More of that later.

Tom's Top Tip
The worst thing you can do with injured cows'
or bulls' feet is leave them, because they never get
better on their own.

I used to trim the sheep's feet in their field with my trusty penknife, but a couple of years ago I got sent a proper pair of clippers by a nice chap called Ethan Rooke, who I think took pity on me cutting my hands up. Then I spray them with blue spray on the back end to show that they've been done. Sort 'em out, spray 'em up, see ya later! I usually find a few overgrown toes, so it's nice to clean them up and make the sheep a bit more comfortable so they're not stood on the toenails. Sometimes you come across an abscess which I clean out, trim round it and treat with antibiotic spray.

While I try and do as much as I can myself, sometimes foot trimming doesn't go to plan. Back in 2019, Mr Neptune managed to break the cow crush in about four places. So the next time I trimmed him, when he went lame, I got some help in. Ross has a tilting cow crush, which is exactly what you need for a big lad like Mr Neptune. It does exactly what you might think, picking him up and tilting him so he's resting on his side. Four rubber clamps hold his feet, which doesn't hurt him. Then you can get to work on all four feet if you need to. That time, Neptune had an overgrown back right hoof and white line disease going on underneath (where the side or wall of the hoof is separating from the sole, caused by damage to an area called the white line region), so Ross had to remove the loose horn, spray some iodine and sprinkle salicylic acid to a raw area and put on a bandage. He also applied a block to the sole of Nep's healthy back left hoof to lift it off the ground and give the other back hoof time to heal.

I love watching a trimming pro at work, because I feel like I learn so much. Although sometimes I completely forget to concentrate on filming it – sorry about that! As a farmer, you're always learning and you do definitely pick up skills treating injured animals, although for anything complicated that requires 'going in', I'll call Oakhill Veterinary Centre (who we've been with as long as I've been around). But for fairly uncomplicated things to deal with, like milk fever, I've learned how to spot the signs before it gets too serious and treat it myself with the right medicine.

Milk fever happens due to a lack of calcium in a cow's blood. During the drying-off period – the chilling out time/ holiday that we give them two months before they give birth, when they're munching on some grass and not being milked – cows don't need much calcium and they actually stop producing it naturally. When the cow calves, her need for calcium suddenly doubles, but especially in older cows who have had a few wee ones, this process sometimes doesn't happen quickly enough. It's not that common – it only happens maybe once for every 20 cows on our farm.

One of the first signs is that a cow might be walking around a bit groggy, like me after a few beers on a Saturday night. After that, the poor girl will lie down and will struggle to get up because she just doesn't have enough energy. She also might develop an S-shaped kink in her neck and her ears will feel colder than the rest of her. So if the signs are there, I know I need to administer calcium intravenously. First, I prep the calcium bottle by attaching the tube to the opening, so the whole process can be as fast as possible. I inject it into the milk vein, which is a large blood vessel that you can see clearly under the skin on the cow's belly. The vet will always use the jugular in the neck, but I haven't quite mastered this yet and it's probably not the best time to practise when you have a cow down.

So, first you crack open the needle, look for the vein and make absolutely certain there's no air in the pipe. And you make sure you keep the bottle elevated. After injecting her with that, she should be up again in about 45 minutes. Sometimes you can see that it's already working even before the whole bottle is in, which is a relief for me, let alone the cow. One time, while I was putting the second bottle under the cow's skin, the calcium that I'd just injected in her vein must have started working, because she got up and ran off! I eventually gave up on administering the last quarter of the bottle because, well, I was dealing with a mobile patient, who was obviously feeling a lot better.

The last thing I do is give the cow a warm glucose drench (using an old Pem's milk bottle, of course), which works a bit like an energy drink to give her an added boost. Usually by this point, her ears are nice and pricked again, and warmer, so job's a good 'un!

> **Tom's Top Tip**
> Put the calcium bottle in warm water to take the chill out of it, so it's less of a shock to the cow.

Prevention is much better than cure, though, so I usually spend a bit of time administering a bolus on an older girl before she calves, just to be on the safe side. A bolus is like a little pellet that goes down their throat with a special applicator gun. The bolus ends up in the cow's rumen – the largest of the four compartments of its stomach. On a big girl, the rumen can be up to 225 litres (50 gallons), which just for reference is well over double the size of a petrol tank in a Range Rover!

We had a Charolais calf with bloat a few years back, which was the first time I'd seen it in a calf on our farm. Bloat is basically lots of gas becoming trapped in the cow's stomach, and it's usually caused by some kind of infection. I'd been letting the gas out by inserting a flexible tube down the calf's throat. It's amazing how far the tube needs to travel to get to the right place, but as soon as it's there, the gas starts whooshing out. Smells great! But I spoke to Andy at Oakhill to ask his advice and he thought a bit of pneumonia might be causing it, so we gave the calf antibiotics and an anti-inflammatory/painkiller, both of which we already have here on the farm, for three days. If it wasn't getting any better after that, Andy suggested we'd need to put a hole in its side to let the gas out. Fortunately, we didn't have to do that – in the end, the drugs and the tube seemed to knock the problem on the head and the calf made a good recovery. Phew! When I put the video out about the calf with bloat, it was amazing to see how different guys in agriculture treat bloat, though. Many folks swear by apple cider vinegar, quite a few others suggested natural yogurt. Someone even told me to crack an egg and feed it to the calf, but I ignored that one!

Occasionally, Oakhill do need to send someone over, though, like when we had a poor Charolais calf (a different one to the calf with bloat) with a swollen face. Luckily, Katherine the vet figured out it was infection by going into the mass and drawing out a lovely mix of pus and blood with a syringe. Horrible, I know – you've got to love farming! Then she went in with a small scalpel to drain the rest of it before spraying it with Blue Spray, the antiseptic wound cleaner that for very good reason is commonly known as farmer's friend. After a good couple of weeks drinking from a teat – because she wouldn't take milk from the bucket – the calf was looking much better, though.

Sometimes we have to deal with more serious injuries, though. Sadly, another time, a Charolais bullock had broken one of its front legs, and front legs are always a bit of a nightmare because that's where cows bear most of their weight. When something like that happens, I think most farmers would put the cow down – it goes with traditional farmer wisdom of 'Your first loss is your best one.' But my instinct was to try and fix it if we could – I'm a big advocate of giving an animal a chance even if the odds aren't in your favour. So I asked Andy the vet if we could mend it and he said, 'We can give it a go – it might work, it might not.' I thought, that's good enough for me, so he reset the joint, fitted a cast around it, splinted it and we raised up the injured leg. It cost around £300, and I know it was a gamble. The bullock could very well not have made it, so we would have ended up paying £300 plus an additional £60 to put him down. And the pessimist in you might say, 'Well, it's going to die anyway – it's bred for beef', but people do whatever they can to save dogs and cats, and I figure it's not that different – I care about my animals.

We put the bullock in the sick pens next to the parlour so I could keep an eye on him and give him some TLC. I gave him anti-inflammatories and painkillers every day for a week after the operation and, slowly but surely, he got stronger and started putting on weight. Then, six weeks later, he was back with the other calves, bouncing around. He went on to live another two summers on the grass. Yeah, it was a bit of a gamble, but he recovered and had a healthy, peaceful and happy life here. I'd make the same decision again even if that bullock hadn't made it. To be honest, it's probably the most rewarding part of the job, when you help a sick animal back to health. It's always worth the extra effort you put in. And I'm reminded of that whenever I look around the farm.

Number 212, although she's better known as Tilly to her mates, is the softest cow in the world and turned six the other day. But when she was a calf, she wouldn't drink water and this was during a baking few weeks in July. She started to go downhill, so I gave her milk in the morning in a bucket and then four times a day I'd give her warm water in a bottle and teat. We did that for three or four weeks in the end and it worked – she's now the happiest cow on the farm and whenever I'm in her field or shed, she'll come up and stand waiting patiently for her daily scratch. She's had four calves now, a healthy number for her age, so she's more than repaid us! And it just goes to show that the little bit of extra effort and that chance you give an animal makes all the difference.

One thing that does happen from time to time is the emergency call from the Ginger Warrior when I'm three beers in at the pub and a juicy burger is about five minutes away from arriving. One such time, 23 young stock (aged nine months to a year, so the cow equivalent of teenagers) somehow managed to escape the field we'd put them in, so Dad sent up the Bat Signal to everyone – me, my sister and my brothers-in-law. Before I knew it, I was shouting, 'TAXI!' at random cars in the street outside the pub. All of us converged on the farm from different directions in different vehicles (me in a Lytham cab) and went looking around everywhere, including woods, wheat fields and buildings. Dad finally managed to find nine of them and get them back, but seeing as we couldn't see anything, we decided to leave the rest until the morning, figuring that they'd all huddle up together somewhere. But then, on the way past one of the big sheds in the rented fields, we saw 14 pairs of shining eyes pointing towards us from the middle passageway of the big shed.

Panic over, disaster avoided and straight back in the taxi to the pub and to my pint and meal that Jo's family had got the kitchen to keep under the heaters for me. Oh, I forgot to mention, the meal I left was my sister-in-law's engagement meal. But, fortunately, they have all been around me long enough to know that cows escaping is a *drop everything you are doing and go to* job!

There are quite a few times when something like that happens and you're left scratching your head and asking, 'How the hell did you end up there?!' That's what happened the time that Harriet the Highland got her head properly stuck in a feeding trough. I say *properly* stuck because she'd got stuck earlier that week (someone had left the gate open – how many stories of balls-ups on a farm start with those six words, I wonder?) – but managed to wriggle free. No such joy on this occasion, though. If she didn't have big horns, this wouldn't be as much of an issue, but Highlands do come with their own unique challenges! Me and Dad (I can hear Dad shouting, 'Dad and I, Thomas') tried all sorts to get her out, but it didn't work, so I was going to have to use the angle grinder. On the metal, not the horns! We had to work as quickly as we could because poor Harriet was getting quite distressed. We put a cloak round her head because we didn't want any sparks to go into her eyes and I put a safety mask on, because danger doesn't take a day off. And danger definitely didn't take a day off, because I got kicked in the back of the leg. I'm not going to lie, that one did hurt. And just when I was a few millimetres away from cutting through the stall, the angle grinder disc packed up. Fortunately, the Ginger Ninja reckoned he could break it with an iron bar, which he did.

Good job, Father! Harriet trotted off, but headed back as soon as the Warrior brought out a bag of bread. 'We still love you, Harriet,' Dad said, giving her a stroke. What a guy.

Although, I have to tell you, I'm not thinking, 'What a guy' when Father sends me down into the slurry lagoon to fix a shear bolt on the slurry paddle, which has stopped turning. When the paddle stops working, the slurry gets thicker and thicker until we can't pump it out anymore. So cue Tom with a handsaw cutting away all the gross stuff that's built up on the paddle, like the string we use to tie the bales. After that, I will always try and pick up the string whenever I see it, because I'd rather not be sawing through it, if I'm honest. There's also loads of long grass, masking tape and duct tape, not to mention cow cleansings, which I'm not even going to explain to those of you who aren't familiar with them, because doing so isn't going to improve your day. My wife is one lucky lady when I come home that evening!

Wisdom from the Ginger Warrior

'My favourite job on the farm? I do love a good drain. If you get your drainage right, it'll work for you 24/7, 365 days a year, and you can farm, farm, farm. So the most pleasurable job I get when I have the time is to go do some draining! I see a wet spot and dive in with a spade and a shovel. Look after the land and it'll look after you!'

Getting my hands dirty in a ditch, dyke or pit is part and parcel of the job. Yes, it's not nice, but someone's gotta do it, although I'm not sure why it's usually me in the muck – especially because my dad bloody loves draining things!

We get a lot of rain in the Fylde, the flat, square-shaped peninsula that our little dairy farm sits on. In winter, it's a bit horrible, but I try and stay positive and tell myself things like, 'Without the rain you'd never see a rainbow.' But sometimes it's difficult to stay positive when you're on a tractor without a cab with a wet arse. Don't get me wrong, we need the rain on our farm to make the grass grow thick and strong, but in some years, the infrastructure that is meant to drain the water away from our fields doesn't. So the land floods.

Under our fields, we've got a number of drains that channel water into two dykes (ditches) running along the edges of our land. The water in these dykes flows into the Main Drain, basically a small river that empties out into the Ribble estuary, about a mile and a half south of us. Annoyingly, though, there are more than a few problems with this system. The first issue is that when there's a very high tide, the height of the incoming tide stops the water from the dykes flowing into the estuary. This usually isn't a problem, but it becomes a major headache when it coincides with crazy rainfall. Even then, there's a system of pumps and gates near where the Main Drain empties out that can force water back into the sea. And this would be great, but this failsafe isn't used enough and the level of the dyke is always too high. So it doesn't take much for the level of water in the dyke to become so high that the water has nowhere to go but back through the drainage pipes and into our fields, and sometimes over the banks of the dyke, too. This is exactly what happened during a couple of the storms in 2020 (and 2012, 2015 and 2018, for that matter!) and we had no chance of getting rid of the water until the level of the dyke went down. Not ideal. The Ginger Warrior and I got quite frustrated by this, particularly because everyone knew that that the heavy rain was coming, so why didn't the Environment Agency prepare for it and make sure that the water level in the dyke was as low as possible so the water had somewhere to go? Very annoying!

Speaking of the Ginger Warrior, he tells me that 20 years ago, the dyke used to empty in at most 48 hours. Now it can take weeks, so we end up with standing water on our fields for the whole of this time when we desperately need to get the grass growing. The weight of the standing water compresses the ground and takes the air out, so it turns into an iron seal of soil where drainage becomes even more difficult. It all becomes a vicious cycle.

And then you've got the contractors, who, a lot of the time, make the problem worse. They'll spend a few days using heavy diggers to scoop out the bottom of the dyke to try and create more space for water to run into. But when they do that, they push the mush from the bottom of the dyke up onto its banks, which is exactly where the ends of the pipes are that flow from our fields into the dyke. So these pipes end up blocked, completely caked in mud and silt. Or completely ripped out by the big machines digging in the wrong place. Oh, and they always do this when the ditch is full. Why the hell would you not do it in the middle of the summer, when the water level is at its lowest and you can see the bottom to make sure you've done a good job?! Sorry for the rant, but I've been around the Ginger Guy with the Moustache too much and it's a very touchy subject around our parts. One year, Dad even locked the gates to the fields so the contractors couldn't access the dykes through our land. He figured they'd only do more harm than good, and you can see he has a point!

When the water level in the dyke does go down, Dad has got a trick or two up his sleeve, like remembering exactly where the drains are under the fields. Just under the surface, he's marked the position with stones, which also draw out the water. And with that intel, we can clear some of the areas of standing water using a stake or a tine (a big metal prong) and a bit of elbow grease. We also used our mole plough (a specially designed arrow-shaped plough that cuts a narrow trench) in late February 2018 – another year when it tipped it down – to break through the top layer of soil, which had been compressed by the water weight, and cut into the layers beneath, so that the water drained away. As the Ginger Warrior predicted, it did help to get rid of the worst of the standing water within a few days, and not a day too soon, because we've always got lots of field work to do in the spring, to make the grass as thick and strong as possible to feed our girls.

Later that year, we also used a sward lifter for the first time since 2012, when we had another year of bad flooding. A sward lifter is designed to lift the ground and put some air into it, so that the water can get to the drains underneath. It looks a bit like a plough crossed with a roller. Three vertical legs cut into the soil and the roller follows behind and presses the opening back together to prevent moisture loss. It's not great for the grass roots, but that's the reason you do it in autumn, after you've harvested your grass for the year. And hopefully it makes the grass grow better in the spring. You always have to think ahead as a farmer – make hay while the sun shines and all that. Unfortunately, we have to take the middle vertical leg off for our little 100hp Hürlimann tractor because it can't cope with all three. We could do with a few more ponies on the farm and not the ones that eat hay.

Wisdom from the Ginger Warrior

'I tell you what – you know your drains, Dad.'

'Well, I've a good idea where they all are. I'll have to tell you one day before I die!'

Amazingly, in 2018, we not only had really bad flooding, we also had the opposite happen in June! We didn't get a drop of rain for six weeks and the grass stopped growing. This is the time that we're grateful to have the dykes – they'll always have some water in because the tide brings it in. My dad tells me the last time it was this dry was in 1976 and they got their tractor driver to fill up the tanker from the pits and dykes and spray the fields each morning. That kept our fields green while others around us struggled. So we did the same thing in 2018, filling up about 15 tanker-loads of water in the early morning so it had time to soak into the roots a bit before it got too hot outside. Although, looking back, doing it at 10pm the previous evening might have been a better idea. There's always next time.

Bear in mind, though, that it's the same tanker we use to spread slurry, so first I have to disconnect the pipe that leads from the tanker to the slurry lagoon. The whole pipe's covered in poo and I get it everywhere each time I move it – so excited for this job, I can't tell you. We won't see the effects of this for a few weeks, but it's the best we can do to ensure we have some grazeable grass by the end of July. Fortunately, though, our third cut of grass the previous year, which we turned into big bales, was quite wet, so it really helped us out that year. The cows bloody loved the stuff. It's funny how the world balances itself out.

We also use this tanker, filled up with water from the dyke, to clean up the second cut shed, after it's had young stock or Highlands in, to prepare for cut grass coming in again. We fix the splash plate (an attachment that spreads the water or slurry out evenly, a bit like a sprinkler) to the end of the tanker, back it into the shed and then blast it with a couple of tanker-loads. Then I go to work with the scraper tractor and the squeegee to push all the muck down the drain. So I've killed two birds with one stone – not only has the shed never looked so clean, I've also thinned out the slurry lagoon with the watery waste from the shed. Pat on the back for Tom!

Sometimes I get to use kit that we haven't used for years, like the side spreader, which, back in November 2018, had been lying in the yard for three years. It was the perfect bit of kit for fertilising the rented fields, which needed a bit of help. The spreader's easily 20 years old and looks like an open-topped trailer which you load muck (or slurry, or whatever you want, really) into. The trailer has a bunch of chains inside that rotate, firing muck out of the side. I remember this video well because it was the one in which I triumphantly told Dad off for not filling up the grease gun after he used it last, only to realise that I was the one who used it last. D'oh! So Dad had a good laugh and I had a good helping of humble pie. I always want to leave these bits in the videos, even if I look like a nob, because, well, I want to show exactly what happens on the farm. And in fairness, sometimes I'm a nob.

Wisdom from the Ginger Warrior

'The muck will provide feed for the worms and the sheep will graze round it, poo and spread their muck all over the field, so all the nutrients get recycled. Then in the spring, we'll get some good grass growth. The livestock under the earth is heavier than the livestock above the earth – and we need to feed them!'

Other bits of machinery only get an airing a couple of times a year, like the haybob, another favourite of Father's. The rest of the year it looks just like a rusty bit of kit by the feed bin, but it's a real godsend. Dad bought it for about £500 over 20 years ago and it works a bit like a combination between a tedder and a rake with two spinning rotors containing moveable tines that fluff up the straw and turn it over to help dry it out. We only need the haybob when we're buying straw off the field. How this works is our neighbour rings us up to say that they've got 35 acres of, say, spring barley straw that they've just combine-harvested and do we want it. Sometimes, like in 2018 when we needed more straw, we say yes and then use the haybob to turn the straw and fluff it up to make sure it's dry before baling. The bob still works fantastically and only costs a bit of diesel and a bit of time. We could get a contractor in to do it, but there's no point when we can do it ourselves and save £50 or so.

When you're using the haybob, you need to go at a steady pace in the tractor – 11 km/h (7mph) or so, which keeps the straw in nice rows for the baler to follow up. There's no point giving it any more gas, because the straw will blow all over the place. But if you get it right, you'll get a few bales' worth of good straw, nice, dry and perfect for bedding up. If you don't use the haybob before baling the straw, you'll end up with damp or wet stuff that congeals together. Which means that you end up either putting most of it onto the midden and spreading it on the fields, or spending ages peeling bits of hay off to help it dry and make it usable. And as we all know by now, because the Ginger Warrior says it a fair bit, waste is cost. So a few hours on the little haybob can save days of man hours during the winter.

Sometimes we've got bits of equipment that we've lent to other farms and then, Dad, nice guy that he is, has forgotten to ask for it back. That's what happened a couple of years ago with the power harrow (and whenever someone says *power harrow*, I hear it in the voice of the guy who did the voiceover on *The X Factor*) that had been sitting on someone else's farm for eight years! I love the chance to learn new things, so if a new bit of kit (or new-ish . . .) comes onto the farm, I'm all over it. We decided to turn a 4-acre strip of land on the fields we rent, which was being used as cover crop for some local shooters, into a nice grass pasture. We got a contractor in to plough the strip and we rolled it to level out the lumps and bumps. Then we fired up the power harrow so it could do its thing, smashing the soil up to turn it into a better seed bed for the grass.

I got very excited about the second-hand (although I reckon it may have been more like tenth-hand) post knocker we bought that same summer. We gave it a blue paint job and it looked as good as new, though! What would usually be a good ten minutes whacking the post with a big hammer now takes a couple of mins with the post knocker. This one's also got two hydraulic systems – one for up and down and another for correcting an angle if you've started knocking it in wonky. And that can happen. We use the post knocker quite a bit now when a cow, bullock or bull decides to try and jump over a fence, and that's more often than you might think. And instead of clearing the fence like a good escapee, they tend to take out the fence and a couple of posts for good measure. What can I say – some days the old expression 'Never work with children or animals!' does make sense ☺.

Since the YouTube channel started to pick up, though, we get sent bits of kit from folks who have been watching the videos – which is just amazing, by the way! Like many farmers, we don't have too much spare cash – we normally budget for about £2,500 of new kit a year. Sometimes it's a little more, but we have to be careful with every penny we spend.

One of the guys who did send us something was Pete from the agricultural supply company Carrs Billington, who had seen Harriet the Highland getting her head stuck. So he had a 'tombstone' feeder delivered to us, which made me happy for lots of reasons. Firstly, it immediately transported me back to my 13-year-old self eating a Chinese takeaway in front of the TV on a Friday night and watching The Undertaker of WWE wrestling fame performing his legendary 'tombstone piledriver' finishing move. I had the time of my life! But, for those of you who have no clue what I'm on about, this particular feeder is so-called because it has a tombstone-shaped metal bar (with one vertical joint running from the top of the curve) extending from the ring at the bottom. It's a modified ring feeder basically, with 12 feeding stations that are designed so cheeky Highland cows can't get their heads stuck anymore. After a bit of coaxing with some cake, the Highlands took to it perfectly. And anything that makes my life easier on the farm makes me a very happy boy.

> **Tom's Top Tip**
> If life has taught me anything, it's that if you want a person or a cow to do something, give them cake!

In 2020, we were lucky enough to get all sorts of useful bits. Alliance Tyres sent us some new tyres for the Manitou, which, given that the tyres were so bald that they were basically F1 racing slicks that Lewis Hamilton would have been proud of, was most welcome. Roadrunner, who are just up the road in Preston, supplied and fitted them (thanks, Dan!), and they're the guys who usually help us out if we've punctured a tyre. Alliance sent us their 323 Agro/Industrial tyres, and I couldn't wait to see which puddles I could get through with them on! It was pretty amazing to have some tread on the tyres for a change. And then, Dan came back a couple of months later thanks to Kirkby Tyres, who'd seen the Manitou video and got in touch to help out giving the Hürlimann a bit of a facelift. They sent us their Agristar II tyres, which basically turned the Hürlimann into an absolute beast.

I'm going to single out 27 January 2020 as one of the most exciting days I've had on the farm, and you could probably tell that from the fact that I said the word 'excited' 11 times in the first 100 seconds of the video I posted about that day.

I even titled the video 'Best Day Ever' and brought my digital SLR camera along to take some snaps. I've wanted this bit of kit for as long as I can remember working on the farm and any livestock farmer will back me up on this: a cow brush! Now I realise that if you don't know what a cow brush is, you'll be thinking, why the hell is he getting mad keen on a brush? And in fairness, you'd be right, because the name 'cow brush' doesn't really do it justice. In fact, it's a monster mechanical cow brush that attaches to your shed, hopefully doesn't knock your shed over and lets the cows scratch themselves to their hearts' content. It makes the cows happy and cleaner, and it improves their health and most probably the quality and quantity of the milk they produce.

To make matters even more exciting, the guys at EasySwing, who make some pretty amazing cow brushes, had heard my prayers for one. It might have been the moment in a video I did of the Dairy-Tech event when Jo asked me where I was taking her and I whispered, 'I've found a cow brush' like an excited toddler on Christmas morning. So EasySwing got in touch and asked if they could donate a cow brush. That wasn't the hardest question I've ever had to answer. Er, yes, please! The good folks at EasySwing – Marco and Finn – installed it in front of what can only be described as a beaming madman. It's a really clever design, with the brush parts made of lots of interlinked circular discs rather than just a single brush, so you can take off the discs at the ends, which get the most use, and replace them with the bits from the middle, which don't get as much use.

So it lasts longer and means you don't need to replace the whole thing if part of it breaks. It only has one bearing to grease, too, which you only need to do once a month, so it's easy in terms of upkeep. When it's assembled it weighs 60kg, which sounds like a lot, but as Marco from the manufacturer EasySwing explains, it needs to be that much 'because your customers can weigh as much as 1,500kg . . .'. We put it up on the outside of the Highs building and planned to move it if it looked like the shed was struggling with the battering that it was about to get. And in ten mins, the brush was up and we had our first cow customer – Heidi (number 9), who started off slightly nervously but then went to town. The only slight issue was that the cows loved it so much that the whole shed started moving, so I had to call my welder and get him to strengthen the steel work. A big thank you to Mayo Cow Comfort for supplying it to us and Chris for coming down to help put it up. Driving past later on in the Case, the cows were bloody loving it, and Mr Neptune too. What a day!

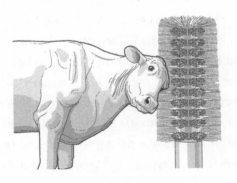

When summer came round, four months later, EasySwing and Mayo Cow Comfort were kind enough to send me another cow brush, but this was a Totem brush, designed to use in a field. We decided to put it in the field next to the horse paddock so people can see it when they're coming out of the farm shop. Chris and Kayleigh from Mayo Cow Comfort turned up and then Chris and I got the shovels out and started digging down so the base would fit in place. Then it took both of us to turn the massive screw that corkscrews 1 metre into the ground. Glad I had my Weetabix that morning. At that point, we suddenly found ourselves with an audience of about 20 cows, who were either just nosy or impatient for us to get a move on assembling their new cow brush. When all the bristles and bolts were in place, precisely 14 seconds later we had our first customer. And then soon five of them were fighting over it. But still, it's a lot better than them rubbing against my poor fence posts.

Just before Christmas Day in 2020, we had a surprise delivery from Finland. That's right, Santa brought us some Finnish chocolates and an EasySwing calf brush because he didn't want the calves to feel left out on all the brush action. Amazing, although Dad had the choccies away pretty quickly. Thanks again, Marco and Finn from FinnEasy. The first cow brush video was the first one I'd made that had gone viral and FinnEasy are getting bigger and bigger as a company, which is amazing. Putting up the calf brush was a bit trickier. Where's Chris from Mayo when you need him, eh? The Ginger Warrior and I just about managed to attach it to the one of the girders in the show room (one of the calf sheds that we used when Can-Am, the all-terrain vehicle company, came to the farm for an event, so now it gets called that as a joke), using a couple of bits and bobs we'd found around the farm. Although I did keep getting jumped on by one calf who was perhaps a little too keen to use the new merchandise. In the end, we gave them some cake and moved them behind the gate to stop the monkeying about. But when it was up, they couldn't get enough of it. It's such a good idea to have a mechanical brush rather than an electrically operated one, because you do without the cables. And if it's one thing I can tell you about calves, it's that they'll chew anything, so doing without electric cables is a very good thing.

This kind of amazing gift makes me so grateful for my YouTube audience, because they have made it all possible. The channel has also put me in such a fortunate position to make some additions to the farm that I've thought about for ages. And in spring 2020, I was able to make my first big buy. No, not a 3.2-litre Ford Ranger Wildtrak, which has been a big dream of mine for some time, but something equally sexy – a feed bin! Our old one was completely knackered, we bought it second-hand about ten years ago and, although it served us well, it was basically being held together with gaffer tape, and you had to bang it with a spade or a long wooden plank to help get the meal out. Oh, and it had about eight holes and a couple of cracks in it (although some of those may have been my fault when I accidentally clipped it with the tractor), so the meal was getting trapped to the side of the chute and coming out manky and mouldy. The whole bin swayed a fair bit in the wind, too, so we had to attach it to the steel column on the side of the clamp with straps. So, all in all, about time for a new one, I reckoned. I really wanted to invest in the future of the farm and I knew this feed bin would last 40 years. And although it felt like a sensible decision, being in a position to make it made me so happy.

I wanted a local company (using local suppliers is something I feel passionately about), so we went with Collinson, our closest feed bin manufacturers, who are only about 20 minutes away and they agreed to take the old one away, too. Knowing that the bin was going made me want to clean up the whole area around it – out with the old, in with the new and all that – so I blitzed it, and then a whole bunch of other stuff around the farm too. I must have been well excited! When Victor turned up from Collinson the next morning at 8am sharp (that's what I like to see), he absolutely smashed taking down the old one. 'Your old bin is like jelly!' he said – I think we made the right call…

So first up, a few days before the new bin arrived, we needed to pour the concrete that it would sit on, so it would be at the right height, with the chute angled over the fence to dispense the meal from. We did it this way because if we had the chute facing the other way, towards one of our fields, the cows would suss where the grub comes from and would be right there. All day and all night. We made the slab wider than we needed in case we decided to stick a molasses tank or something similar there later. The Ginger Ninja got stuck in with the wellies, helping to smooth out the concrete, and then we wrote on the name of my nephew Freddie for good measure. You've got to put your stamp on it. Which is exactly what a duck decided to do later that day, stepping on the still-wet concrete – thank you, Mr Duck. Again, it sounds daft that I would get excited about such an odd thing, but it felt like a really big deal. It was my first proper purchase on the farm and the first time we had poured concrete for years, after all. Although, as you'll soon find out, we've been doing a fair bit of concrete pouring recently, too...

We ended up with a green colour for the bin – pretty much British racing green, which the Ginger Warrior pointed out matches the slurry tower nicely. I got well excited when it arrived because it was so shiny and clean, and there's not much of that about on our little farm. It's a bit smaller than the last one but it holds more (not sure how that works, but I'll take it). There's even a window in the side so you can see how much meal is in there and we won't get mouldy stuff stuck in the side – nice. You can take the bolts out of the window and power-wash it clean, which you're meant to do every year, if you really want to.

One big extra surprise was Collinson's prototype FeedAlert system, which weighs how much feed we're taking out of the bin at once. That means we can be much more precise about how much feed we're putting into the Keenan mixer feeder. Another thing it does is let you know when the amount of feed in it goes below a certain amount so you can order more in. The chute's even got a lip on the back so you can hook your bag over it. Amazing. The Ginger Guy with the Moustache wandered over just as Victor was finishing up putting it up. 'I think it looks absolutely superb. The house that Tom built! I think we'll find it's a good investment you've made for the farm. I really appreciate it, thank you very much.'

I found that moving, particularly because, like a lot of folks, maybe we're not that open with our emotions as a family. Maybe we don't tell each other how proud we are, that we're a bit worried about something, that sort of thing. That's just the way it goes. For whatever reason, we are a bit more free sharing our feelings with people outside the immediate family. With my dad, I know how proud he is of me and I think if the subject ever came up with him, he'd say something like, 'Well, why would I tell you? You're doing a good job and you know that.' He's taught me to be self-sufficient, has given me the space to make my own decisions and he trusts me to do things properly. And I'm proud of all those things.

A lot of people ask me if my dad and I ever fall out. We might have a little bicker (although Dad would disagree with that word and replace it with 'a healthy exchange of opinions'), but he and Mum are incredibly supportive of me, and I'm so lucky that way. Dad knows that I'll take over the farm one day and respects that each generation leaves their mark on it, the way that he did. I think generations of Pembertons have grown up with their fathers as their role models, and they respect the past and look to the future as you have to do on a dairy farm. And that's why I can't wait for the moment when the new shed is done and me and my dad sit in the middle looking out at our cows enjoying their plush new gaff with a beer in our hands.

3

THE FARMING YEAR

Maybe slightly confusingly, I'm starting this in April, not January. But there's method to the madness. I wanted to begin on one of the most exciting days of the year for a dairy farmer whose cows graze outside, and that's the day when we open up the gates and let the ladies out! Cue hundreds of cows running around like kids in a playground. We turn it into an event at the farm and let people in the local area know when it's going to be – usually a Saturday in April after we've had a run of warmer weather. Now, every year, more and more people turn up and form a line along the fences ready for the countdown. Sometimes it gets a bit nerve-wracking because I start wondering if this is the one year that the cows don't skip around for joy when I let them out. So I find myself saying encouraging things to them beforehand like, 'Come on, girls – it's your time to shine.' And luckily they do – they never let me down!

The cows know something's up around turnout time because their usual morning routines are disrupted while we make preparations. I'm busy doing things like clipping their tails so they're nice and tidy and clean, giving them their annual vaccinations, checking their feet to make sure that they're walking fine on all four, and giving them an overall medical to make sure everything's looking good. And then I'm out in the fields picking up anything on the ground that might cause them a problem and checking the fences are secure. Because the one issue we have on turnout day is that cows always run to the borders next to the fences when they're let out and, being herd animals, you end up with other cows forming up behind them and giving them a little nudge. The Ginger Warrior used to warn me each year that this could happen, but I could never truly picture it until it actually did occur one year and we ended up with a fence knocked down and a bunch of escapee cows on an adrenaline high.

Wisdom from the Ginger Warrior

'It's never the first cows out that knock the fence over because they'll stop just before it. The second lot behind them are a bit slower and nudge the first ones, but it's the third and fourth line of cows that don't stop and push them all over. It's a bit like watching one of those coin-pusher machines you get at the seaside amusements.'

Maybe they feed off how excited I am too, because there's definitely more mooing than usual that morning. That moment, when we open the gate and watch the cows bouncing around on fresh grass while people clap and cheer, gets me every time. For the calves, this is the first time they've properly seen grass and they jump up and down like animals in a Disney film. Meanwhile, the older girls might be a little bit slower out the gate, but they're no less thrilled to be back on the grass. Does anything beat a 600–800kg (1,300–1,750lb) cow jumping off all four legs with pure joy?!

For me, this feeling has been building up for some time. I've had a hand (quite literally in some cases) in each one of their life cycles. As I write this now, I've got one cow, number 236, who is due to give birth to a calf in a few months' time. That calf will be the first short-horned cross on the farm. The mother is only two months into pregnancy, but I can't wait for that calf to be born!

To help the transition from winter feed ration to spring grass, which is great for energy but not so much for fibre, we give the cows a buffer feed, which is basically like a dietary supplement. Another reason we do this is to make sure the cows aren't having to deal with a major change to their routine. What the buffer feed consists of depends on the quality and quantity of the third cut of grass we did last autumn and turned into silage.

The idea is that this buffer feed gives them a more balanced diet with the fibre they need so they can produce butterfats, the stuff that makes your milk and butter taste great. But it doesn't always work – some cows will just walk straight past the buffer feed and back into the pasture. Maybe I give them too much of an option, but if they're happy, I'm happy.

Soon after we let the girls out in the spring, we usually have them strip grazing to give them an extra boost each day on the freshest part of the grass, and by that I mean grass at its most nutritious stage. Strip grazing involves using a moveable electric fence to cordon off a strip of grass for the cows to graze on and then moving the fence every few days to allow them access to a fresh strip. Then the bit that they've just grazed has time to recover. It's a great way of prolonging and maximising the yield you get from the land, because the pasture will become denser the more it's grazed. It also gives you, the farmer, control over exactly what the cows are grazing. And to try and improve that a bit more, in June 2021, as part of our Countryside Productivity Small Grant application which I'd sent in back in November 2020, I'd got a portable solar-powered fence energiser, which generates 0.4 joules to power the electric fence we use for strip grazing. I check to see if an electric fence is working by holding a bit of grass on it. The Ginger Warrior has other ideas and usually tests it by gripping it in his hand. But this time he nudged it and, well, let's just say he won't be doing it again. 'I feel like I've been on bloody *Casualty* attached to the paddles' were his precise words. Amazing. And the sun wasn't even out – it was a typical overcast day, so it wasn't even properly powered. Plus, we later realised that it was on its lower power setting, so when it's set to wild-animal mode, it's going to be like the fences in *Jurassic Park* (when they're working, anyway). Also, it'll charge itself, so we don't have to keep messing about checking and changing batteries like we have done before, or finding that the fence has been knocked over because the battery got short-circuited. So, a good buy – and doing a wee bit for the planet, too.

People often ask me if I'm a tractor guy or a cow guy and I never know what to answer, because I'm happy with both, to be honest. But there are moments when cow work wins, like the joy I get from knowing how happy the cows are going to be when they come onto fresh grass. Just like turnout day, they're all there waiting by the gate while you start putting the electric fences up – they know something's up and they're excited! I reckon the older cows are telling the younger ones that it's going to be a good day today.

The first thing to do when putting up an electric fence is to create a straightish line, which the Ginger Guy usually does by driving the Kawasaki Mule (our little four-wheel-drive utility vehicle with a door that has a mind of its own) into the distance before heading back. At one end, you stick a tripod with a corkscrew on the end into the ground to hold it firm. The electric line attaches to this tripod and your battery connects to the line via a crocodile clip. Then you put rods in the ground every ten or twelve strides and attach the electric line to each one. The other end of the line (with a rubber ring, which works as an insulator) usually goes around a fence post but, classic Father, he often can't find one near enough so he uses a tree branch instead. Does the job, though! Dad usually starts putting the rods in the end closest to us, and I'll walk to the far end and start from there because I'm youthful and have newer knees. Actually, maybe that isn't true – Dad's had a knee replacement, so his knees are newer than mine! And that's it – job done. Unless your battery and the replacement you brought along both fail on you, which they did the first time I filmed strip grazing. Nightmare.

Wisdom from the Ginger Warrior
'Rather than carrying a whole bunch of fence posts and stopping every time you need to push one in, put a load down every 60 yards. It's like putting supply depots down the line like Scott of the Antarctic.'

So, every day we normally move the fences 10 yards or so depending on amount of grass the cows have left. That way the cows can smash that new area while the bit they've just grazed takes a breather. I love the sound of cows crunching and munching on that fresh leaf. And you can tell that they've all massively enjoying it because all of their heads are down, except for one that's usually having a lie down and eating at the same time. Now that's what I call efficiency.

April's also the time we start rolling the fields for the first time that year. We use a 2-metre roller and pull it at around 8km/h (5mph) in the tractor. We have a 2.5 metre one as well, but it leaks a bit of water and doesn't do such a good job. The first thing I can tell you about rolling is that it's a boring task. It's steady, slow and, wow, this is making me tired just thinking about it. When you're a youngster starting out in farming, it's often the first job you get trusted with.

I used to hate it but, a bit like a fine wine, time has matured me and now I quite enjoy my time rolling. Part of the reason for that change is that I feel like I'm not using that much of my brain when I'm rolling, so I can do something else at the same time, no bother. Like thinking about everything I need to catch up on. Or making a video and flying a drone into something. And sometimes, there's no substitute for belting out a few banging tunes in the cab when I'm rolling – you've got to love a good singalong with a bit of '90s punk rock. And in the tractor cab, it's like singing in the shower – no one's judging you!

But if I'm having a really bad day – let's say I've just ballsed something up royally and then I have to jump in the tractor to do some rolling – I try and change my mindset by listening to something that will make me think. For me, that's usually a podcast. I'm lucky to have the time and space in the cab to learn something or see things differently, and if I'm listening to motivational stuff, it'll have a really positive impact on me. Some things I've learned alone in a tractor cab have had a big influence on my life. I've learned to value my failures, because if you don't fail, you won't grow. Most of the time it can be better to fail rather than doing something right the first time you do it. If you nail it the first time, you won't have learned that much about what can go wrong or how to cope with it and fix it if it does.

I listen to a lot of famous speeches when I'm in the cab, and one that really stuck with me was Denzel Washington's commencement speech to the University of Pennsylvania in

2011. He said, 'Fail big!' and 'Every failed experiment is one step closer to success'. I don't mind failing on the farm – it happens every day in some shape or form and I'm happy to share that with you. Life isn't pretty a lot of the time – it's hard work, you bugger things up and sometimes you get a bollocking. But it's all part of the journey of getting things right, bettering yourself and feeling like you've earned that brew at the end of the day.

So, I often come out of the tractor cab in a much happier mood than when I jumped in. And I really try and keep that positive, cheerful mindset around the farm, because not only does it keep you motivated, but it also means you're likely to spread that message to other people. When I get back home, I'll make sure I post about that day, but I'll do it in as positive and cheerful a manner as I can because I know people are thinking, 'Well, that guy has bad days but he's still positive', so the minute they have a bad day themselves, they don't think 'Oh God!'. I just try and be who I am and if it makes someone else feel better about that day or have a bit of a laugh, I'm well happy.

With rolling, you're levelling the ground off. We have to do that because the animals have made lots of ruts (especially the Highlands, who do like to make a mess. And don't even get me started on the horses) and we need to even it out. But also, pressing down the grass makes it come back up thicker. You have to pick the right time to do it, though. If the grass is too long, you just end up flattening it rather than evening out the ground, so it's a waste of diesel and time. Also, this might be kind of obvious to some of you, but make sure you don't go through any big wet areas on a field, because then you just end up with a mud-caked roller and a pissed-off father. I learned that back in crazy wet 2018, when my slightly OCD *need to roll every corner* got the better of me.

Rolling is just one of the many things we do to help grass grow; along with harrowing and fertiliser, it all plays a vital part in helping to feed our cows. I'm a big believer in putting in 5 per cent more effort here and there, because you can genuinely end up with a 25 per cent better field. It's all part of the marginal gains theory I mentioned earlier. You can find that your extra time, care and attention have been worth their weight in gold and will have a knock-on effect improving your grass and your cows.

MAY

In May, we'll usually mow our first cut of grass that year (we generally do three cuts in total during the year). The Ginger Warrior makes the call, but we know it's happening before he says anything. That's because, when my sisters and I were growing up, on a certain day in the late spring we'd always see him lacing up his work boots in the morning. That's the signal that mowing's happening. These boots are easily 30 years old and he gets out his shoe horn to lever them on. It always puts a smile on our faces!

We try and start the first cut when the grass is at the right stage of growth. It needs to be full of leaf and really dark green, which means it's full of energy and hasn't gone to head yet. That just means that it hasn't developed seed heads, which is the point where the grass is getting more stalky at the bottom: that's great for fibre, but not for energy. So if you leave it too long and the grass has gone to head, you'll have to buy energy in, usually in the form of brewer's grain, a by-product from the breweries. And that's an extra cost. Annoyingly, though, sometimes the fields are at different stages of growth, so in 2018 we mowed 60 acres when the weather was nice, put it in the silage clamp, rolled it and sheeted it up. We then mowed the rest two or three weeks later, so we had to take the sheets off again, which every farmer knows is the biggest pain in the arse in the world, but hey ho. The grass had started to go to seed, and when that happens the quality starts to dip but the quantity goes up. Sometimes that's a good situation to be in, because the stalkier stuff will make good winter feed for the heifers and dry cows who don't need as much energy from the grass.

Mowing is a really exciting day for me and any lad on a farm, because you get to drive big tractors. I'd say mowing is probably my second favourite job in a tractor behind slurry carting, but I'll get into that later. It also means that summer's properly here, so I'll put the headphones on and have a bit of a dance! God, I love that smell of freshly cut grass. Last year we used a loaned Case 145 Maxxum tractor on the farm instead of our Hürlimann. While the Case doesn't turn as well as the Hürlimann because it's got a longer wheel base, it is a beast of a tractor with 50 per cent more power. It's comfy as stink with non-threadbare armrests, too. Not to mention suspension that works. And air con! Dad's idea of air con in the Hürlimann is opening a window. And Lord help you if he sees you driving around with the door open. Having said that, I like that I've grown up without all the mod cons because it means I don't miss them. Having the Case felt a bit like going on a nice holiday – lovely for a bit, but you've got to go home at some point.

So, when you're mowing, first remember to fill up the tractor with diesel – always makes it go further. Since I can remember, we've used the JF Fieldfarer 245 mower, which is about 20 years old and had cut a lot of grass in its time, but it did the job. Sometimes the belt would set on fire, though, which wasn't ideal. But in May 2020, just in time for our first cut, the good folks at Malone arrived with a Procut 3000 centre-pivot 3-metre mower, as a loan for the season. And wow, it absolutely minced it, going at just over 14km/h (nearly 9mph) in the Case, compared with 11km/h (less than 7mph) in the Hürlimann pulling the JF mower. You can do 10 acres of grass an hour, and it's a fair bit quieter than the old JF – I could actually hear myself think and didn't feel like my brain was rattling around in my head when the window was open. The only downside was that the Case went so fast that I couldn't fly the drone at the same time – I learned that the hard way, as per. Also, sometimes I missed a bit of grass when I was messing about, like the time I decided to race Dad when he was alongside in the Hürlimann. I know what you're thinking – 'Tom, you're a five-year old child' – and yeah, that's true, but I'm having a good time, people! Totally worth it.

We were so impressed with the Malone mower that we ended up buying it after the demo. The day before the first cut in 2021, we serviced it, checked and changed the oil, sprayed the bolts with WD40 and flipped the blades over (I figured we were going to be doing enough mowing for it to make sense to do this now, although Dad didn't think we needed to just yet). The only minor issue was the fact you don't get quick-release blades, so it's a bit of a faff clearing out the trapped grass and muck and takes longer to change the blades over than the old JF, but hey ho. Servicing it shows you how important it is to look after your machinery.

> **Wisdom from the Ginger Warrior**
> 'Greasing should be done little and often. It's a bit like sex – you don't want it all at once.'

One big plus, which Dad was a big fan of, was the little magnet on the drain plug, which attracts all the iron filings coming off the bearings through wear and tear. Otherwise, those fragments would start blocking the oil feed, get in the gears and cause more wear. 'Every car should have one,' said the Warrior. He'll be doing his own magnetic merch next. After that, the only thing left to do was blow up the rear right-hand tyre, because the heavy mower suspended on that side adds quite a bit of weight. We did get a bit of a telling off from Mother for making a mess of the car park, though. Sorry, Mum! One day, I'll get a workshop and I won't be lying under a piece of kit in front of the farm shop. Just not today.

So our first cut was aboard the Case 130 Vestrum, which we got loaned earlier in the year for a three-month demo. Ooh, that was a gooooood day when it arrived, I can tell you, plus it was exactly what a lot of you guys had been telling us to get in the comments sections of a few of my videos. And I'm all about giving the public what they want! The Vestrum won a Machine of the Year title at SIMA 2019 (the International Exhibition of Solutions and Technologies for Efficient and Sustainable Agriculture – wow, that's a mouthful) in the mid-size tractor category, so we definitely weren't playing games. Annoyingly, while I was messing around checking out the state of my drone, which I'd just crashed into the Collinson's feed bin and broken off three blades, I missed the Case coming off the trailer. But on a plus note, Ross, from Case, had travelled all the way from Bristol to show me how it works. What a guy. I didn't want to get the cab dirty at all, though, so I stripped off for my YouTube fans. I'll just about do anything for those YouTube Views!

It's the top model in the range, and with a 4.5-litre (8pt) engine, it's got a good bit of grunt and torque. The one they dropped off to the farm was a 2021 model with only four hours on the clock (tractors work in hours rather than kilometres or miles), so it was literally brand spanking new. It's got a panoramic roof so you can see what's above you as well as what's in front of you, and that's perfect for loader work. It's also got a side seat, so Joanna was very pleased, and it's even got room for our dog Moon, too. Oh, and it comes with a cool box. Which all made for one happy farmer.

The Ginger Warrior was well pleased as he came down the steps after his first proper go in the Vestrum:

> This is the best mower I've ever used and this tractor, once you get used to it, is the easiest to use. You can turn sharper and there's a lot more torque in the Vestrum than the Maxxum (the Case 145 which we had on hire last year) for its size and power, but that was a fantastic tractor too. Look at the grass now – it looks like your lawn!

Big statements from the Warrior! And that was one of the reasons why saying goodbye to the Vestrum was a tough one, because I think it might have been my favourite tractor we'd ever used here. It did everything we asked it to do, no bother. So when I got an email from Case saying the three-month loan was coming to an end, it was sad times. It feels like I've had two honeymoons this year – one with Jo in the Lake District and one with the Case on the farm! Although, both honeymoons came to a sudden end when I got back because the Vestrum had been picked up when me and Jo came back from the Lakes. I'd forgotten to give the tractor a wash, too, so felt a bit bad about that. Not least because I'd broken my rule that when borrowing a piece of kit you should always try to make sure it goes back cleaner than it came and that it's full of juice. Sorry about that, Case!

Yes, the Vestrum's CVX transmission (which automatically manages the engine and transmission) took a little bit of getting used to – like half a day – especially when you were driving on the road, but it was amazing doing field work. We've got too much flying out of the pockets at the moment to be thinking about buying new tractors. In winter, it's fine, we only really need the Hürlimann because we're not really doing any field work, but when next summer comes around, we'll need two tractors. If we were in a position to get a new one, I would probably go for the Maxxum because you've got that extra power with the 175hp engine. And no one in the history of tractors has ever said, 'Oh, I wish I had less horsepower to do this job!' It also means you've got all sorts of options, like attaching a mower to the front linkage. It would have been amazing to see if we could run a front mower together with the side mower, because we could really smash through the mowing in no time. But is it worth the extra £10,000 to use it four or five times a year? The dilemmas of being a dairy farmer!

But anyway, I'll wipe the tears away and we'll go back to the first cut on the Vestrum. And this might sound familiar by now, but later that day I crashed my brand new drone again in some trees. It was only seven days old, so I think that makes this crash a new record. I had to call my cousin Ben, who's a tree surgeon (shout out to HMA Tree Care), and he asked me if I wanted to go up with him and get the drone from the top of the tree. Er, no thanks, mate! I'm terrified of heights and, well, that drone was *high*. When Ben turned up, he drove up in... a Unimog – an absolute beast of a truck made by Mercedes. Seeing that Unimog brought back some amazing memories of a whirlwind experience back in June 2019, when I got one of the best phone calls in my life. The conversation went something like this:

Mercedes rep: Would you like to come to Austria, all expenses paid, and drive Mercedes Unimogs and G-Wagons to celebrate the fortieth anniversary of the G-Wagon?

Me: Er, let me think about it for a second... Austria here we come!

Although the trip got off to a bit of a bumpy start when I got stopped by security twice. The alarm went off for the suitcase with the drone in because there was something suspicious on one of the batteries. So they swabbed it and it turned out to be... cow poo. Amazing. Then I got stopped again going through the metal detector because I forgot to take my belt off – classic Tom.

Things improved when we were met by a convoy of bangin' G-wagons outside the airport, though, and we got driven up to Mercedes' test track in the mountains. Never in my life will I feel like James Bond more than I did in that moment. And we're talking a test track with a 52 per cent gradient when you're on two wheels – mental. For the whole two days I was there I was thinking, 'How is this happening to someone like me?' I couldn't understand it. But I had the best time ever. I did my best not to look shit scared getting into the cable car at the end of the first day, but thankfully we weren't that high up. On the second day, I didn't get to drive the Unimog because I don't have a truck licence (f***!) but, wow, it's not playing games, tilting at up to 40 degrees and smashing through rivers. I loved the 1979 one we went in – it's all gears and levers, no buttons, no electrics – boom! Then I got to drive the G-wagon on the test track, which included an 83 per cent downhill gradient and a completely nuts rocky climb upwards. Terrifying moments, but I'm living my best life!

I think we mow a little differently to other folks when we're doing two fields next to each other. We 'open the fields up' by starting with the outside and do seven circles, before turning round and going once backwards the long way round the way the tractor's already been. Then I go into the field next to it and do the same with that one before coming back to the first field to finish off the middle. We do it that way to avoid constantly lifting the mower up and down and catching the sward of grass that we've just mown. I know folks will say I'm wasting my time going in and out of fields, but it doesn't take me that long. That's Dad's way and, to give him props, it's a good idea and makes sense to me.

A lot of the time, mowing takes all day, but sometimes I'll have help, like when my cousin turned up in his Massey because his girlfriend was in Dubai and he was bored! I've done more than a few solo mows where I've been out all night. It's not great on your back when you're sat in our old Hürlimann, and you get well hungry. Luckily, Jo usually turns up with a tuna melt from Subway to keep me going and sits in the side seat, even answering Snapchat and Instagram messages for me. Top wife points. My sister Penny's saved the day with a bag of grub a few times, too.

> **Tom's Top Tip**
> When you're on the tractor at night, stick a plastic white bucket on the edge of prominent obstacles so the light from the tractor shines off it and you don't end up crashing into equipment/buildings. Trust me – I've learned the hard way.

The day after first cut (or sometimes later the same day), Dad gets to use one of his favourite pieces of kit: the tedder, which works using a bunch of spinning forks that shake the grass about and dry it up. In June 2021, Malone made good on their promise to loan us a six-rotor tedder for the season – it was a sweetener after we bought the mower from them the previous year. And the Ginger Warrior bloody loved it.

It's got seven tines on each rotor instead of the usual six, so you're getting one-sixth more turns, which means you can go a bit quicker in the tractor. But the crucial thing to me is the hooked tines instead of the downward-facing ones, which sweep the grass up into the air and it lands completely and utterly spread. It leaves a nice swath. Like a carpet. It's sweeping rather than raking. Plus, the forager isn't under the same strain as usual. Last thing: you're getting maximum drying. It's a pleasure to work with, this machine. There's just that little bit more metal – it's built up to a standard and it's doing a good job. You wouldn't like it on the end of your nose for a wart, though.

It's great to see the Ginger Warrior happy with the new bit of kit. It's whether we can find the cash to keep it, that's all. We've got a few big things going on at the moment that might make it tricky, though. We'll see.

After tedding out the grass, we get a contractor (Cornalls) in to row it up using a windrowing machine to rake the cut grass into lines (windrows) using a number of spinning rakes. In 2020, the rowing-up man from Cornalls asked us if he could use the windrower to make a message of thanks for the NHS from the Cornalls and Pembertons Farm, which I'd film using the drone. Dave Cornall has four nieces and a daughter who work for the NHS, so props to those guys. The year 2020 had been an incredibly hard one for everyone, with fires in Australia, floods in the UK and a worldwide

pandemic, so it felt like a great way to say a huge thank you to all NHS staff and key workers from the farming community.

After the windrower's raked the grass into neat lines, it makes it much easier and quicker for the forage harvester (we just call it a chopper) to do its thing, both hoovering up the grass and chopping it up finer. With the new tedder from Malone, though, the windrowing and foraging become simpler because they're not having to deal with as many clumps. So the rowing, carting and buck-raking boys are all spending less time on each field, saving man hours. And man hours = cash!

Next, we pour an additive solution into a compartment in the chopper, which sprays it onto the cut grass. This helps the fermentation process, preserves the grass better and increases the quality so your cows like munching on it. And I'm glad it does all of that, to be honest, because additive must be one of the most expensive things you buy on a farm given how tiny the pot is – like £50 for 50 grams – so when I spill a bit, we're talking about pounds not pence trickling away.

The chopper blows the finely cut grass out via a chute into a big trailer that you pull up into position alongside it with the tractor, and you collect it as the chopper moves through the field. So you've gotta make sure you keep your speeds the same. You really don't want to cock this bit up because you'll end up with grass blown all over the shop. Once the trailer's full, you tip the grass into the silage clamp. Our outside clamp is a decent size – 30 metres long by 14 metres wide and

3.5 metres high or so, and 100 acres' worth of grass goes into this clamp. That's a good 800–900 tonnes, easy.

In the past, depending on how much grass is coming in, we've also used the indoor shed, AKA the 'show room', next to the clamp from July to October (it gets used as a shed for young stock from October to April). To be honest, though, it's a nightmare of a clamp to work in, with upright steels placed everywhere. Also, the roof is too short, so you have to tip the grass in front of the clamp before pushing it in. This is why we've built the new second-cut clamp (more on that in Chapter 6). And the indoor shed, which we can't actually get to any more anyway, will become the new parlour. At some point!

Before we tip the chopped grass into the clamp, we clean up the space with the Manitou bucket and fix two drainage pipes along each side wall to channel the moisture away so we don't get any gross sludgy bits where the water's been trapped.

Next up is buck-raking, which involves a big-ass tractor/loader with a long-toothed rake attachment for packing the grass into the clamp. The massive tyres help to squeeze the air out of the grass, too. We get a contractor in to do this because you need the right kit and someone who knows exactly what they're doing. Shout out to Dave Cornall and his JCB! Then the Ginger Guy with the Moustache goes to town with either the Hürlimann or the scraper tractor to roll the silage using the tractor's tyres. You cannot get Dad off the clamp until it's perfectly rolled and there isn't a bump visible anywhere. He's doing that to compact the grass as much as possible, which reduces the chance of spoilage. And as we all know, waste is cost. Dad gets very excited when the grass sticks to the tyres of the tractor, because it means it's dry and full of sugars, which is just what you want.

Sometimes I'm allowed to roll, but it's a bit stressful because I know how particular Dad is about his rolling. So I want to do the best job I can, because it makes him happy. For the first cut in 2021 over the road, we had a whole team of Cornalls over and Dad didn't need to roll it because we had Andrew from Ashcon using the silage compressor/compactor – a roller made out of scrap train rails. And Dad absolutely loved it.

Wisdom from the Ginger Warrior

'I always say that silage is made in a clamp not in a field, and the best thing you can do for it is roll, roll, roll. Squeeze the air out and squash it down flat. Your biggest losses can come from the smallest area, so attention to detail is really important to make sure you look after what you started with!'

The next job is sheeting up, which we try and do as quickly as possible, because as soon as you've stuck the mower on, the grass starts deteriorating. Also, the last thing you want is rain to come tipping down just after you've spent ages tedding the grass to get the moisture out! Sheeting up is up there with the worst jobs on the farm, but we have to do it because we need to create an airtight barrier between the grass and the outside. If you don't do it properly, you're going to end up with a lot of spoilage, which the cows won't eat. So why does no one like sheeting up? Because the tyres that you use to weigh down the sheets are normally filled with horrible, and I really mean horrible, liquid! And also it's back-breaking work. Want to get fit in your life? Go round all the farms and help them sheet up for a week. Friday won't come quickly enough!

First we cover the grass in a waterproof polythene sheet. And here's a good moment to mention the first rule of sheeting up: don't stand on the sheet! Then we cover the black sheet with a green sheet, which is made of knitted mesh to stop birds and other wildlife getting stuck in to the grub beneath. It also adds more weight to the black sheet to squeeze out more air, so we don't need to cover the surface in quite as many tyres, which is the final job, to weigh it down even more. We start by chucking tyres on to the sides of the clamp, then cover the back of the clamp and make our way forwards. (Boring) job done. Except, sometimes, that's not quite the end of the story.

Back in August 2018, I was blasting through some of the last jobs on a Friday so I could leave just after five to head off to a stag do. Somehow, the gate in front of the clamp didn't get shut (I'm not naming names, although I tell you that the culprit's name wasn't Tom) and I came in on Saturday morning, a little the worse for wear, to find a scene of absolute carnage. Over a hundred cows were in the clamp. Tyres everywhere, sheets torn, silo nibbled, hay bales knocked off the trailer and pee and poo all over the shop. It looked like they had had a proper night of it – the stag do I went to was tame by comparison!

Yeah, it wasn't the best thing to face with a steaming hangover, especially because it came off the back of a few other mistakes recently, but I think everyone has a bad run of things from time to time. You've just got to keep going forwards and tidy up the mess. So I restacked the hay bales, moved the tyres, shifted some of the silo that wasn't going to keep to give to the cows, used the Manitou with the shear grab to cut a clean face on the clamp so it was nice and compacted again, re-sheeted the clamp and cleaned up the mess with the scraper tractor. At the end the place looked better than before! I did worry about what it would look like when we opened it up again. And then, a few weeks later, we did, and it looked like a horror show at first. Mould everywhere. But thankfully it was only skin deep.

JUNE

After mowing and sheeting up the clamp, the next field work we'll do depends on what the weather's been up to that year. Back in early 2018, we'd lost around 10–15 acres' worth of grass in the floods, which left the fields with loads of horrible bare patches. So, after we'd mown and sheeted up, we needed to get grass seeds down in those patches and harrow them in. If we didn't, those bits would just end up full of weeds, which would spread.

Usually we'd harrow beforehand but the soil was too hard, so first Dad went round in the Hürlimann with the spreader attachment to put the seeds on. This time we went for quite a large ryegrass seed, which is great for areas that need regeneration. Plus, it'll suppress the weeds. Luckily, we already had the grass seeds in the barn and, as Father says, 'There's no point leaving them there in the bag – they won't grow there – so they want to be on the field and let nature take its course.'

After spreading the seeds, Dad headed back to the farm and attached the Dutch harrow, which has lines of downward-pointing spikes (tines) fitted to a heavy frame. This helps push the seeds down a bit to give them a good chance to germinate. Behind the lines of tines on the harrow is a crumble roller, which presses down the undersoil to give you a nice, even seedbed which will retain moisture and help the seeds along. The roller also lifts and puts air into the topsoil, which helps everything along too. The Dutch harrow is one of those pieces of kit that lives around the farm and doesn't move for years. But then you pull it out, smash 15 or so acres with it and it goes back away. Yes, it looks like a rusty piece of scrap, but it's worth its weight in gold for when we need it.

After we've used the Dutch harrow, we stick on the heavy roller to level the ground. It takes at least two weeks for the seeds to germinate and soon after that we hope to see a nice growth of grass coming through. We know that we won't get a big second cut from it later that year, but it is a longer-term solution, to recover all of our wet spots and make sure we've got some good grass for next year. Sometimes after a setback like the heavy flooding, your focus has to be recovery and investing for next year and the year after. What we really needed, though, after we'd reseeded, was a little bit of rain. And I know that sounds ridiculous just weeks after going through some of the worst floods I've ever seen, but when you need it, you need it. Fortunately, if there's just one thing you can guarantee about farming in the UK: it will rain again!

Unlike 2018, in 2019 we hadn't been underwater for the early part of the year, so a week after mowing the first cut we were out on the fields spreading slurry. We do this to help the grass grow so we can get some nice new grass for grazing and to bulk up our second cut. This might sound odd to some of you, but slurry spreading is one of my favourite jobs on the farm. I know that the effort I put in is going to be rewarded and you can see the difference it makes to the fields. It also feels good to get some of the muck out of the slurry tank, watch the level in the tower go down and put it back into the ground. You feel like you're cracking on! Although I realise that I'm in the minority in the Ag community, because in the very official social media poll that I did, back in October 2019, posing the question 'Do you prefer grass cutting or slurry spreading?', only 37 per cent of people said slurry. Maybe I'm just a massive loser. It's quite possible.

In June 2019, the store was full of muck, but it was quite

watery because I'd been pressure-washing the AI stalls (artificial insemination stalls, where we serve the dairy cows with bull semen) and calving boxes while it'd been dry and nothing had been in there. So I turned the paddle on in the slurry store, then switched on the pump that sends the slurry from the store into our big circular slurry tower via the big pipe over our heads (I told you we get a lot of muck). My plan was to empty about half the slurry store into the tower, then turn on the pump that sends slurry from the tower back to the store via a pipe underneath us to thicken up the stuff in the store. Then I'd pump the slurry in the store into the tanker. Still with me?

Tom's Top Tip

Don't leave the pipe that connects the slurry store to your tanker while the paddle's on. Because when you come back and find a squashed tube wrapped around a paddle, you look stupid. Believe me, I've done it before...

The only problem with this job (other than what I just mentioned) is that it does whiff a bit. And usually the wind takes this waft towards the farm shop customers. Nice.

The next thing to do is stick the back-end splash plate on the tanker to distribute the load evenly, so each bit of grass is getting a good bit of manure. And then hopefully we have a nice bit of rain come down and wash it all in.

> **Wisdom from the Ginger Warrior**
> 'You should always spread slurry in the rain: it
> washes off the leaves and down into the grass roots –
> ideal! And make sure it comes out the tower like
> a nice gravy.'

Sometimes we hire in a tanker to speed things up with slurry spreading, like back in 2018 when we got hold of a 2,500-gallon tanker. I carted it, while Dad drove our 1,600-gallon one. Thankfully I was a lucky, lucky lad that year and got to drive my cousin's Massey (while he was away). And at 170hp (he'd chipped it, which means that he's had a power chip installed, which alters the tractor's power and torque settings to optimise its performance) it goes like stink and feels like it's not even pulling anything. It's also so much comfier than the Hürlimann.

And then, in June 2020, I was able to make my biggest investment in the farm to that point: a brand new 2,400-gallon slurry tanker. I figured we needed a new, bigger tanker that would last us for the next 20 years at least. So we traded in the other two slurry tankers we had on the farm – the old PrimeX 1,500-gallon one and the 1,600-gallon TST one – to the dealers, Clarke & Pulman. Dad and I kept our trip to the PrimeX manufacturing unit to see how the new tanker was coming along secret. Not even Mum knew what we were up to. When we drove over, Dad told her we were just over the road feeding the cows!

We'd already trialled a few tankers, which was a useful process because it made me realise which bits of which tanker I really liked. In the end, we went with a PrimeX, the guys who made the last one we bought that we've had for 23 years. It still has the same pump and we haven't needed to weld it yet – the only thing we've changed is a couple of tyres and the splash plate, but those bits of kit take a hammering. Also, PrimeX aren't far away from us, and you know us – buy local! All of the guys involved in the sale are British companies and we're proud to support them. The wheels are supplied by Kirkby tyres in Liverpool, PrimeX are in Preston, just 25 mins away, and Clarke & Pulman, who supply PrimeX's machinery, are based in Ormskirk, between Preston and Liverpool. It's also very useful being able to drive to PrimeX quickly to sort out a problem if you have one – we can even drive there with the tractor and tanker – or want to add an adaptation, like a dribble bar, which we did in June 2021 (more on that in a bit).

The guys at PrimeX designed the new one to our own specifications, which was awesome. Dad really wanted it with a barrel thickness of 8mm (while normally tankers are around 6mm thick) and PrimeX seemed to be the only manufacturers offering a 2,400-gallon tanker in that thickness. Over to the Ginger Guy: 'It may add to the dead weight with the tanker empty, but the number of extra years we'll get out of it, the strength of the thing, must outweigh the cost of a little more metal going in. You're getting something 33 per cent better with 50 per cent more life on it.'

Fair enough, Father. Although, just so we've got it written down for the record, Dad also sort of admitted I was right about where to put the filling points. A truly massive day.

We over-specced the new PrimeX mainly because it can get so wet at our farm: we added properly big-ass Alliance tyres (which Kirkby Tyres, who are supporters of the channel, were kind enough to help with) and hydraulic brakes, which are a first for us. The tyres can travel at 40km/h (25mph) with just over an 8-tonne load and at 50km/h (30+mph) with a load of below 8 tonnes, so they're smashing it really. Not that we have a tractor that can do 50km/h (30+mph), but here's hoping, Father! The tanker's also got an 11,000-litre (2,500-gallon) pump (oversized for the size of the tanker) to make it quicker to fill up, an oversized outlet at the back to help with cleaning it out and a hydraulic changeover valve, which saves time, although Dad's not a fan because he still prefers to do things manually. It was amazing getting to see the tanker at different construction stages, and it was coming together nicely with all the bits we'd asked for. It was also useful because we could make decisions there and then, with it right in front of us about, say, which side we wanted the slurry tube on. Dad was really keen for it to be on the right side – he'd been driving tractors so long looking to his right towards the controls and where the mower or topper's mounted that he can't look to his left any more without turning right round.

About two weeks later, I could see the new PrimeX on the back of an HGV driving down Ballam Road. What a thing of beauty. Quick – fire up the drone! Then I did the honours backing up the Hürlimann and bringing it home before Richard, the Clarke & Pulman rep, showed me all the features that I didn't even know it came with as standard. He also taught me what some of the bits on the old one are actually for – every day's a learning day and all that!

When the new shed went up in 2021, we took the opportunity to sort out the slurry system, which had been a bit of a pain the arse for some time. So, we invested in a new smart aeration system from a company called Dairypower. In the base of our main slurry store, which holds just over 1 million litres (220,000 gallons) of slurry, we screwed on 16 separate air lines, which will pump air into the slurry six times a day (we'll set it to go off five times at night, on the cheaper energy tariff, and once during the day so that we hear it go and can make sure it's still working). This ensures that each load that comes out of the tower is the same from the first to the last. So why do we need this? Well, slurry is a bit like raw milk (stick with me). When raw milk is left for a while, the cream comes to the top and that's why we always shake it before we put it on our cereal. It's similar for slurry – you get a thick crust on top but, unlike raw milk, you can't just give it shake. Instead, you have to bring in a contractor with a huge tractor and a slurry stirrer, which is expensive. Also, the slurry will start to separate again the minute the contractor leaves, so we try to time it for when we are spreading and we have to stop everything.

With this new system, yes, you need to fork out the big one-off payment, but it takes the expensive cost of calling in a contractor away. In the long run, it should only cost around 50–60p a day to run, which is amazing. On top of that, you'll get a much better slurry consistency and the new system is better for the environment because it emits 30 per cent less ammonia into the air. Overall, it's a big win for Team Pemberton.

I get a lot of questions about slurry, believe it or not. The first one I get asked a lot is why do we overlap when we're spreading it rather than just spreading in nice lines that meet each other? Well, it's partly because the Ginger Guy told me to and he's the boss! What he'd say, though, is that we like to get to the end of the field in one full load, and that involves travelling a bit quicker and overlapping. Also, it's harder to get stuck in a wet patch if you're travelling faster and, believe me, you don't want to get stuck with a tanker in a wet field. Also, our slurry tends to be quite thin – the joys of having an open yard! – so we want to get as much as possible on.

The next one that loads of people ask me (mostly non-Ag folks or farmers from abroad who do things differently) is why we don't spread to the edges of our fields. The answer is I would if I could because I'm a bit OCD like that, and it would look a lot neater on the drone, but you're not allowed to spread slurry too close to a footpath. Them's the rules (!) and you have to follow certain rules if you're claiming the Basic Payment Scheme (which replaced the Single Payment Scheme/Single Farm Payment) from the government. I can tell that Father is itching to speak about this subject (I'll give you the keyboard in a minute, Dad).

Basically, we're in a seven-year transition period after Brexit and they're reducing payments to farmers each year until 2024. After that date, they're replacing the Basic Payment Scheme with 'delinked' payments until 2027, when they're cutting all support. It's a very difficult time to be a farmer, to be honest. All sorts of things are going to be changing about the way you're allowed to farm your land and this includes the way you spread slurry. Over to the Ginger Warrior:

> It's always easy to point the finger at farmers for all sorts of environmental issues and all farmers are tarred with the same brush, whether it's arable or livestock. The problem with the Single Farm Payment is that the people who least require it seem to get the most from it. It means that cash-rich farm businesses can 'land bank' (not farm the land but keep it with the intention of selling it later for development) and take the Single Farm Payment while the farmer with 50 acres who is working the land would still be struggling even with the payment.

When the payment goes completely, many family farms like us will struggle and, unfortunately, I think we'll see many smaller farms leave the industry and get swallowed up by their bigger next-door neighbours. And the knock-on effect of that is that we're likely to see fewer cows grazing outside, because bigger businesses tend to favour keeping animals inside for cost and space reasons. While I'd be sorry not to see more cows out, I understand why some farmers choose to keep them in.

A few things I can tell you about slurry spreading, mostly what not to do! The first thing is the old farmers' wisdom of 'Don't drive where you've spread slurry' and it's bang on because it makes a mess of the grass underneath and your tractor gets covered from the tyres flicking it back up. Second thing: Don't wear any clothes under your boiler suit that you want to wear again. Third thing: Don't leave the back window of the cab open when the wind's gusting about. Fourth thing: I know I'm not a big fan of gloves, but there have been times when I'm trying to pull levers on the back of the slurry tankers using a piece of wood. Would have been a lot easier if I'd brought a pair of gloves. I know what you're thinking: why's Tom worried about a bit of muck on his hands? Well, he's not, unless it's the start of the day and he's going to be in the tractor cab for the rest of the day spreading muck everywhere and stinking the place up. On that note, getting the end of the slurry pipe blocked with hay or finding there's a stone stuck in the chute of the splash plate aren't the best things in the world, I can tell you that for free. It's funny, you know – Jo never seems to join me in the side seat of the tractor when I'm spreading slurry . . .

In early June 2021 we had some good news about bringing in some new kit that was going to improve things a lot on the slurry front. Back in November 2020, before we finally decided to go ahead with the new shed, I'd applied for a Countryside Productivity Small Grant (CPSG).

Tom's Top Tip

Small disclaimer about this one: I may have got this off the Ginger Guy with the Moustache. Before you back up in the tractor towards the slurry tank, stick an old fence post (or something similar) where you want your back wheel to be. Then you'll feel it and know where to stop so you can attach the pipe. You'll also know you're not going to reverse into a gate. It's a godsend, believe me!

This is something the government provides to help farmers buy equipment that improves 'technical efficiency, animal health and welfare, resource efficiency or nutrient management'. And in June 2021, I found out that my application had been successful, which was amazing. The main reason I applied for the grant was to help us finance a new dribble bar for the PrimeX tanker. A dribble bar gives you so many improvements over a splash plate, which is what we had been using and which you keep hearing rumours about being banned at some point in the future.

The splash plate has worked pretty well for us on the farm and it works quite simply, basically firing out slurry in a wide arc. The trouble is, while it's cheap and easy to use, a lot of the nitrogen that you want going into your soil is actually being released into the air, particularly when it's a windy day (and we do have a few of those up here). And that means your grass (or other crops) isn't getting the nutrients you want it to have, so you have to use fertiliser to help the grass come along nicely. It's also a bit of an arse because the wind fires off the slurry in all directions, so you have to overlap and go over the same ground, which isn't great for the soil (or if you don't want your neighbours to complain). And last but not least, the stuff that's going into the air is ammonia (a compound containing nitrogen which accounts for around 50 per cent of the total nitrogen contained in slurry), which causes serious environmental problems, including acid rain.

What a dribble bar does is deliver a controlled amount of slurry to the grass roots, and the benefits of that are massive. Firstly, you'll be able to get your cows grazing the grass a couple of weeks after you've spread slurry down (assuming you've had a good bit of rain, and that's one thing you're pretty sure of up here on the Fylde coast) because the dribble bar has spread the slurry in deeper lines, so it's not contaminating the upper leaves of the grass. That compares with waiting at least six weeks to graze your cows after you've spread slurry using a splash plate, especially when you're spreading the thick stuff that we were in June 2021. Secondly, you're cutting down on ammonia emissions by around 30 per cent (because ammonium, the form of nitrogen we want as farmers to help grass grow, is going directly into the ground rather than being released via a splash plate as ammonia gas, which isn't what we want), so you're being a lot kinder to the environment. You're also saving on buying fertiliser, because more nutrients will have gone into the ground. Thirdly, you can go faster on the tractor when using a dribble bar, so you're saving time. The fourth thing is that it's not affected by the wind. Actually, there's a fifth thing, too, and this might benefit me more than it does you. The two arms of the dribble bar, when they're in the horizontal position, swing inwards if you bang it against something, rather than causing either it or anything you've crashed into on your farm serious damage. Works for me!

The one problem with the dribble bar is the cost. But when the government can contribute 40 per cent of it, which is what they offer with the grant, that's a nice big chunk out of an item worth £10k. So I went for a Mastek Vertical Dribble Bar, and I just really hoped that the Hürlimann would be able to pull it, although at 450kg (1,000lb) it was one of the lightest on the market. If the Hürlimann didn't pull it, we'd have to buy a bigger tractor. Usually, I'd be jumping up and down about that, but given how much we're forking out for stuff at the moment, it would have been a right pain!

When the dribble bar arrived on the farm, Mark and Ben from Mastek went about fitting it to the PrimeX tanker, which I'd cleaned out the previous week so it'd be in good shape for them. But then I realised that Dad had been out tanking a couple of days after that. D'oh! So when they removed the splash plate attachment, slurry went everywhere. But, after that little hiccup, Mark was well happy with the PrimeX tanker because it's got more space for extra pipes than other tankers. To be precise, he said, 'This was the best one I've ever done' and it was on after 20 minutes. Yes!

The dribble bar comes with the Mastek Supercut Macerator, which smashes through any bits of straw or other long fibre that might get into your slurry, using six serrated cutting blades. It's a clever bit of kit because as the blades turn (don't put your hands anywhere near this!), they block some of the 28 outlet pipes while pressurising the others. Which all means that you end up with an even distribution of slurry coming out of the pipes. Each outlet pipe also has its own air supply, so if there's a blockage for any reason, it'll only affect one of the many pipes.

Bringing the dribble bar up from horizontal to vertical is pretty cool. It reminds me of a supercar with gull-wing doors. Plus, it folds the dribble bar away nicely, so you don't really even notice it when you're looking in your wing mirrors on the road. If you do notice it, it means you've still got your dribble bar set to horizontal, so stop your tractor and sort out your life!

So, the first test run went great, not least because the Hürlimann pulled it fine, which was a bit of a relief. Also, the tanker was still clean after using it, unlike with the splash plate, which does throw the slurry about everywhere. Then Ben showed me the Mastek app, which works a bit like a calculator, getting you to input info about the size of your tanker, the amount of slurry you want to spread per acre and the time it takes you to empty your tank, then it'll tell you how fast you need to be travelling in the tractor. This makes it more accurate with every load. We also get our slurry tested, so I can tell you how much nitrogen is in each 1,000 gallons of slurry. Which in turn means I can also tell you how much nitrogen each acre of our land is getting through slurry and bagged fertiliser. Amazing!

The first proper day on the job playing with my new toy, though, everything went wrong. I couldn't get my drone up (that's what she said. I had to get one in the book) because I got a notification telling me I wasn't allowed to fly it over this airspace. That's usually because BAE Systems, just up the road, are up to something. It was a bit of a bummer, to be honest, because I would have loved to get some aerial shots of the first dribble bar outing. But then the pipe connecting from the slurry tower to the tanker got blocked and the Wareing guys accidentally went through a slurry pipe outside the tower with the digger. Then something didn't feel right about the dribble bar – it just didn't seem to be working right and the slurry was coming out super slowly. So I rang Ben at Mastek and he told me to check out the stone collector to see if anything had got stuck, and I discovered that a bit of plastic guttering had got sucked up. It was useful in a way, though, to find out where problems can occur in your kit, so I know what I'm looking for in the future if something like this happens again. Later, one of the 28 trailing hoses stopped working (right in the middle), so it was leaving an empty space where no slurry was coming out. Not the end of the world, but a bit frustrating because I didn't know what was causing it.

A couple of weeks later, I drove the PrimeX with the dribble bar and the Ginger Warrior took another tanker we'd hired in with the splash plate. We wanted to tank like men possessed because the rain was coming a couple of days later and we wanted to completely empty the slurry tower. While we were doing the first few loads, we had Hoyles Contractors in to stir the slurry in the tower and sort out the big crust that had formed on top. They use a long propeller to smack into the crust and stir it all up so the consistency is much more even. Because when you've got a big crust, you've got loads of thin stuff at the bottom, and that's not what we need when we're tanking. We like a nice consistent slurry that isn't too watery and isn't too thick. And with the new aerated Dairypower system, this shouldn't be a problem!

I did get a stone stuck in one of the dribble bar hoses when I started tanking, but they're actually really easy to take on and off. I pushed this one back in to the macerator, hoping that it would go through to the stone trap underneath, which it did. Job done. There was another blockage a bit later in the day, and this one was harder to fix. I took the hose off (one of the yellow ones at the end that dispenses the slurry) and got the pressure washer involved to try and clear it, but no joy. So I had to take off the metal bit where the end of the red hose meets the yellow hose: I found a big clump of mucky grass and, thankfully, that unblocked it. But what a faff!

I got some good drone footage of the dribble bar and then of me and Father tanking the same field in our two tractors with a dribble bar and splash plate. I was a lot happier using the dribble bar because I'd got used to it, plus I'd got some top tips on how to use it from Farmer Phil (thanks, mate!).

Between me and Father, we nearly managed to shift 300,000 gallons of slurry in 36 hours. Not bad going.

Wisdom from the Ginger Warrior
'I think the dribble bar spreads it faster than I can with the splash plate. It's not covering the grass, which is the most important thing – it's putting it on the roots – and there's no smell with it. It's the way forward.'

Usually by the end of June, around six weeks after first cut, the slurry's done its magic and Father starts thinking about putting his old work boots on again. When to start second cut can be a bit of a dilemma and depends on what the weather's doing and whether or not some fields are further along than others. In late June 2019, the 7-acre field had gone mental and the grass was already knee-high! So that year, we decided to cut early, while the weather was with us. A lot of farmers will do this, go when the weather is good, because you don't know if you will get a chance again for a few weeks. And that way, you end up with good aftermath grazing for the cows and the grass comes back quicker underneath. Because we'd had a great crop of first cut grass, in terms of quality at least, we wanted to focus on chopping some high-quality stuff for second cut so we could cut down on some of the expensive stuff we buy in to mix for winter feed – cake, Selco and fodder beet. As the Ginger Warrior summed up perfectly:

'You can do a lot with a little bit of good, you can't do a lot with a heap of s**t.'

So it was all go until a sealed bearing disintegrated on us in the JF mower and the belt came off. At least it didn't catch fire this time! Legend that he is, Dad still had the JF logbook in perfect condition, so we knew what to get to fix it, but we weren't up and running for another 20 hours or so. Nightmare, but these things happen with old machinery. Next year didn't start much better for second cut – we had weeks of rain, so had to delay until mid-July, although we did have the new Malone for the season. After a few teething problems with the mower mowing too short, we lifted it up a bit and cracked on for the next two days. What a difference the Malone made over the old JF, especially with the grass this long. We always say that you know you're going to end up with a big crop when the grass heads are flicking the top of the mower.

But then, when it came to rowing it up and we thought we had a break in the rain, it started pissing down just as the contractors were buck-raking the first of the second cut. Nothing for it but to get the covers on and call off play for the day. We got through it the second day, though – the clamp was full and the grass was nice and dry-ish. We've got a drain running down the side of the clamp, so any moisture should find its way down there. And then Dad did what he does, jumping on the Hürlimann and rolling it like a man possessed until there wasn't a breath of air in the entire clamp. One thing I did miss a bit for second cut 2020 was the Case tractor, which we'd just given back. It was bang on size-wise and comfort-wise, but I couldn't complain with the Hürlimann – it did the job as per and I smashed 65 acres in a day, no bother. We were helped out by the A-team (Heidi and Jack, who handle some of the drone footage when I'm busy and volunteered to help out with sheeting up, although I'm not sure Jack knew what he was in for) that year to sheet up both clamps and stick the tyres on. Job done, or so I thought, until Dad said we might be sticking the third cut in here. Sheeting up is bad enough, but imagine taking the sheet off one day, chopping grass and then having to sheet back up the very next day!

Tom's Top Tip

When you're mowing, get your earphones in and your ear defenders on top. Boom! Cuts out all sound. Props to my friend Ross for that one.

The last week of June sees the build-up to a special day for our community on the Fylde coast: Lytham Club Day and Rose Queen Festival. The day itself is on the last Saturday in June and was first held in 1894. It's a day of fun for all the family, with lots of events, a fair and a parade of floats. We'd never done a float before, but in 2018, the year after we opened the farm shop, we decided to get properly involved. So we got ourselves a trailer, attached the Hürlimann and spent a few days getting it all ready. My brother-in-law Des and the farm shop manager James set up a little pen, filling it with straw bales and adding acrylic and soft toy farm animals. And they made a little barn out of leftover pallets and a garden path complete with front door and a flower bed to look like a doorstep milk delivery. Plus we had a BBQ cooking sausages in the sun. I even dressed up in a latex cow costume and waved to everyone from the pen as we went along the parade route, while Des, Penny and the team handed out leaflets and gave sweets to the kids. The Ginger Warrior, meanwhile, drove the Hürlimann. And it was all worth it, people, because we won first prize for the best float. Great team effort!

JULY

Usually in early July, we get the topper on for the first time in the year. Topping gets rid of the pockets of long grass that are full of seed heads, and that's stuff you don't want to silage. Cows are quite picky if they have a choice and they don't like to eat that wiry grass that comes up, so we get rid of it. The topper tidies it all up, so you end up with a nice level playing field. That way you encourage the smaller grasses underneath to grow, which they should do evenly, which is exactly what we want. We used to hire in a topper, but we bought an 8ft-wide Fleming Super Float 800 side-mounted one a few years ago. It has two big circular blades which rotate at high speeds and the main body is mounted on two skids which slide against the ground. You can adjust the height of the blades depending on what floats your boat. I'd go so far as to say the topper is one of the best purchases we've made for the farm. It does everything we need it to do and I love using it. Which is why you'll find me at 5pm on a Sunday in the summer using it when I probably should be at home. There's something about seeing a big thistle poking out ahead of you and knowing you're going to absolutely smash it with the topper – amazing.

But, back in 2018, when I videoed topping, everything went wrong. Before I'd even started, I'd just received a mobile phone bill for £600 for using data on my phone because we hadn't got the Wifi set up yet in the new house and I thought: how much can a few Gb be? A lot, it turns out. Then I managed to hit the tedder driving the tractor out of the yard (it was all right, thank God). Then I mangled the PTO (power take-off) shafts, which transfer power from the tractor to the attachment, mower, topper etc that you're using, because I didn't have the topper high enough, so when I accidentally accelerated too quickly, the front part of the topper dropped, hooked on the ground and flipped up, pulling the PTOs out of each other. What an idiot! But I did manage to sort it without Father's help, which is the main thing. I can't remember if I told him about all of these cock-ups, which might mean he's hearing about them here for the first time.

One thing I've learned is that it's better to tackle topping when it's a bit dewy. When it's really dry, the topper grips quite a lot, so you have to pull it back to the centre to keep an even line. Also, it's very important to grease up the bearings before using it, which costs a few pence of grease instead of having to fork out hundreds to replace a bearing.

AUGUST

Sometimes if we've not had much rain and the grass isn't growing well, we find ourselves having to open up the silage clamp earlier than we'd like to. Back in the summer of 2018, we didn't have a drop of rain fall on the farm for six weeks and we were down to our last three big bales of silo, so we opened up the clamp in August to make sure the girls were all getting well fed. This was a bit worrying because the year before we opened it up a month later, and that time we had more grass in the clamp! Also, if you remember, 2018 was the year that the girls had made a dog's dinner of the clamp after a gate had been left open, and I had to re-sheet it up. When we were forced to open it up again a few weeks later, I feared the worst. Thankfully, although there was a lot of spoilage at the front, there was still some good grub for the girls to munch on.

The first job is to drive over the Manitou and attach the bucket if it's not already on. Then you can toss the tyres on top of the sheets into it and stick 'em out by the slurry tower. Then you roll the sheets up a bit like a carpet and hold them in place with tyres from the top. Luckily, it didn't look too bad at all, apart from a few patches where the cows had trampled and around the wall edges, where you usually expect to see a bit of waste anyway because you can't secure it as tightly to get rid of the air. The Ginger Warrior was well happy: 'It smells gorgeous. There's not an on ounce of waste where they've sealed it properly. It's dry, it smells sweet, succulent, it's leafy and well cut. If you couldn't eat it, you could definitely smoke it. It's absolutely beautiful!' Classic Father. He doesn't smoke, by the way, but it doesn't stop him talking about it!

So we pick up the silage with the shear grab and load it into the Keenan mixer feeder, then add Selco. We usually mix up around 600kg (1,300lb) of silo with 50kg (110lb) of Selco, but this year we added 5kg (11lb) of barley straw that wanted using up because it makes good roughage. Then we unload it into the feeding troughs for the calves, who we still had inside because they were only four or five months old and turning them out towards the back end of summer (when the grazing wasn't great) might have made them struggle to keep growing as we'd like. That mixture of Selco, silage and barley straw (and a bit of cake on top. And who doesn't love cake?) gives the calves a good energy lift and then the cows can tidy up what the calves don't finish when they're done milking. Everyone's a winner.

The next year, it wasn't the cows who got into the clamp early, it was me. Ordinarily, it would have been a completely mental idea to open up your first cut of grass – the best-quality spring grass – just a couple of weeks after cutting it and I did agonise over the decision. But the clamp was so full that there was no room for the contractors to move in and out when it came round to second cut a couple of weeks later. In fact, the clamp was so full that I could barely close the gate or get to the feed tower without leaning over the fence. We figured that someone would end up running into the sheet with the Manitou and tearing it soon enough (let's be honest, there was a high likelihood of it being me), meaning we'd probably have to open it up anyway. So we shifted a good few loads of silage with the shear grab, loaded it into the mixer feeder along with the Selco that Dad had bought for a knockdown price (mainly because it was June and no one wanted it) and gave it to the calves. As Dad says, 'The proof of the pudding is in the eating' and the young 'uns absolutely loved the stuff. So it was a risk worth taking.

Each year, you face a slightly new set of circumstances depending on how warm it is, how much rain you've had and how much grass you've got in the clamp. So we get to a point in late summer before we start the third cut when we ask ourselves which fields do we mow and put into silage, which do we put into big bales and which do we leave for cows to graze? This decision comes down to two things, the first of which means working out how many big bales we need for the year. We feed big bales to our young stock because it's great roughage for them and good to introduce them to a grass diet (with a bit of cake added for good measure). We also buffer feed our cows around autumn with big bales when both clamps are full and we're just not ready to open them up yet.

The second thing to think about is cost because, like every business, a lot of things come down to pounds and pence. Stay with me on this one. To chop the grass like we do for our first and second cuts we pay by the acre. It doesn't matter how much grass there is on the ground, you pay contractors per acre. But with big bales, you pay per bale. We chop first and second cuts because we know they are going to be good chops, but the third cut is always a smaller yield, with some years bigger and better than others. So the decision usually comes down to this: if we think we're going to make less than four bales to the acre we're better off baling, but if we're going to make more than four, we should get the big boys in to chop it – we're going to fill the clamp!

For third cut in 2019, although we probably should have mown two and a bit weeks before, the weather was all good and I'd just come back from a couple of days off for Jo's birthday. It was a Sunday, the sun was out and, much as I like going away for a bit, I love coming back, especially when it's nice and dry, to see what needs doing. I know it was a bank holiday and I should probably have been chilling out or doing whatever young people do, but it was a beautiful day to be farming and that makes me very excited to be in the tractor with a few tunes on the radio. This is what farming is all about to me – enjoying it loads and doing a good job. We had new armrests, too, in the Hurlimann – winning! We hadn't replaced them for about four years.

That year, the grass had come back in a thick sward and Dad was well happy with it, although the JF mower was having some problems getting through it, just because of the weight of the grass. So we needed to mow super slowly, a couple of gears down from usual, at like 8.5km/h (5mph). But as Dad says, 'A bit slower is easier on your back and bottom, especially when you hit some bumps.' It did need tedding out, though, because the grass was still wet underneath. Only 36 hours after we'd started to mow the third cut, the grass had already grown an inch in between the rows, so we could put the cows back on those fields to graze the following week.

It was a different story back in 2017, when we ended up mowing when it was wet, so we tedded it out three or four days later to get it as dry as possible in the sun and with the wind, before baling it a couple of days after that. But it was still wet and a pain in the arse to bale because you're wrapping all the moisture in, so it's a bit like leaving a damp towel in a corner for six months. Not nice. When we opened those bales up the following spring, they were damp, tart and smelled a bit like going-off cabbages, but the young stock seemed to like them (to my surprise) and they'd already had their breakfast. That's quite a good result, to be honest, because the bales could have been a lot worse. Although, having said that, that day I broke my first drone and managed to drag the manky plastic from the bottom of the bale across my face. So let's just say there were winners and losers that day.

Wisdom from the Ginger Warrior

'What a grass-growing year 2019 was – absolutely fantastic! We'd put less fertiliser per acre than we ever had, we'd slurried at the right time and it'd fed the ground well, it rained and the sun was good. Plus we'd put a bit of sodium down, too, which helped the grass grow back. The cows were content and there was green everywhere. Magic.'

August is also the month of #Farm24, which *Farmers Guardian* launched in 2015. #Farm24 is the biggest annual online event in Ag and it's all about promoting farming to a wider audience so we can show people the good that us farmers do on our land, with our livestock and for the consumer. It's usually held on 5 or 6 August and on that day loads of farmers post videos and photos on social media to show people what their typical working day is like, showcasing their skills, enthusiasm and dedication. It's something I feel really passionate about, so much so that I even break my Tuesday, Friday and occasional Sunday video rule to do a video for it.

In August 2020, I did a video on all the little jobs we do around the farm. Things like tail clipping aren't glamorous, but it's one of the important things we do to keep our cows healthy and clean, one of many jobs we do every day to make the wheel turn round. Each year, I also shout out a few social media accounts that I've been enjoying in the past year. I like to think I'm all about helping support and encourage other farmers and Ag workers if I can and the fantastic work they're up to. And if their following gets bigger, we can show the world all the good farmers are doing.

For #Farm24 in 2021, Tom and Anthony from *Farmers Guardian* turned up to do a bit of filming and ask me 24 questions about life on the farm here. Some of the questions are a bit of fun, like what's your favourite thing in the farm shop. And I've got to tell you, the Yorkshire pudding wrap at the hot counter is something else. Homegrown beef,

Yorkshire pudding, cheese and chilli sauce. I treat myself to it on a Friday and it's a proper belly filler. As for what I bring home from the farm shop, it's all about a good steak. I go for a nice rib-eye with a good bit of marbling, but Jo prefers a fillet. And in answer to the cheeky question about whether I take anything from the farm shop without paying for it, well, there might be the odd occasion where a nice-looking apple gets eaten in the shop and then forgotten about. Apples (and carrots for that matter) aren't safe around me!

Other questions I get asked are a bit more serious, though, like 'What's the biggest misconception about dairy farming?' For me, it's the misconception that milk comes from the supermarket, and what I mean by that is it feels like the cows and the farmer get overlooked. Milk doesn't just magically turn up at the supermarket! Dairy farmers put a lot of time, effort and love into producing every pint of milk. We've looked after our cows, produced top-quality grass for them to munch on and given them a happy, healthy environment and we're rewarded for our effort with great-tasting milk. I'm proud of our milk and the mixture of cows we have here – Brown Swiss, Ayrshires, Friesians and Holsteins, who all contribute to the quality of our raw milk especially. I know that a lot of farming folks up and down the country are putting in the same effort as we are here, so when I see milk on a supermarket shelf advertised at a cheaper price than a bottle of water, it does always make me a bit frustrated.

We do get quite attached to our cows here and name them, sometimes after friends, family, vets or visitors! Tilly is my favourite, if I'm honest – she's super friendly and comes up for a scratch most days. When she was born in June 2015 she wasn't drinking any water and was getting really dehydrated with sunken eyes and a shabby-looking coat, so I gave her a bucket of water twice a day for the first eight weeks. That built up a relationship between us, and I think she remembers it, which is one of the reasons she's so friendly. I think every dairy farmer loves their cows. You have to. They're your livelihood and you want to look after them and give them the best life you can. I really enjoy working with animals and the amount of effort I put into them because they reward me for it. All around our farm, I see cows with shiny coats looking well-conditioned and getting their heads down to happily munch on grass. And when I come home in the evening, I get a really good feeling after I've done a hard day's work.

SEPTEMBER

In September each year we have our annual TB check for every cow and calf over six weeks old. Before we started producing raw milk in 2016, we had to arrange a TB check every four years, but now it's every year. It's a job and a half and a major hassle for any farmer because you've got to get all your animals in (and when you've got Highlands, that can be a challenge), so you need a fair bit of help and it all takes forever. But it has to be done.

First Andy (or Suzy) the vet clips two patches of hair on each animal's neck and checks to see if they've got any lumps and bumps in that area (so they're not confused with a reaction to the test), before measuring the thickness of the skin there using callipers. Then he injects two types of tuberculin (basically a mix of proteins extracted from TB bacteria and grown in a lab) into the skin. If any of the animals have been infected with TB, a swelling will appear at the injection site which gets worse 48–72 hours later. So Andy comes back three days later to feel for any swelling.

We are in a low-risk TB area here in Lancashire and any animals we bring onto the farm (which we don't do very often – we only bring bulls in every three to four years) are TB tested before they get here, but it doesn't stop you from getting nervous while you wait for the results. Because if any of them are infected, it's a nightmare. So when we found lumps after the tuberculin test on a couple of our cows in 2019, I did poo myself a bit, but it turned out not to be TB. Phew!

It's not only annual TB checks that you need to be on top of, though, if you want to produce raw milk. The Food Standards Agency (FSA) inspects the farm every six months, but you don't get advance notice of when exactly they'll turn up. Part of the inspection involves providing microbiological sampling test results for your raw milk to prove that it meets a certain standard. There are two different measures used to assess the quality of milk – bacteria plate count and somatic cell count, which basically provide an assessment of the hygiene of your milking equipment and the health of the animals. The plate count measures the amount of bacteria in the milk caused by factors like how clean the teats are or how well sanitised your setup is. With the somatic cell count, a high number of somatic cells (which are formed inside the udders) basically indicates that a cow is suffering from mastitis or another illness, so a low number suggests that the cow is in good health.

We take a lot of pride in the quality of the milk we produce, so we aim for well below the acceptable numbers. That's one of the reasons why it's so important to know your animals and if any of them might be suffering from anything. Because on a small dairy farm like ours, even one or two cows with mastitis can cause a big spike in the somatic cell count that goes into the bulk tank. In the first year of selling raw milk, we came third for the lowest somatic cell count in the whole of Lancashire, which we were really proud of.

We also get an inspection from Red Tractor about this time of year. They happen every 12–18 months, but we've had ours in September for the past couple of years. For those of you who don't know what the little red tractor sitting above the Union Jack is on your bottle of milk, it's a scheme set up in 2000 to help assure customers that they're getting something traceable, safe and farmed with care. As a farmer, you have to follow certain standards to allow the farm to display the red tractor logo, and your adherence to the standards is what the inspector checks. So this is a good opportunity for you amazing folks who watch the channel but aren't in agriculture to find out quite how much we have to do!

Some of the standards are legal requirements anyway, such as all calves born in the UK needing a passport.

To apply for one, you first need to register the birth, so you have the calf's unique ID number. Then you can order ear tags from an official supplier, the first of which (the primary tag) you have to fit within 36 hours of the calf's birth if it's a dairy cow. You have to fit the secondary tag (fixed on the other ear) to a dairy cow within 20 days of their birth. For other cows (beefers), they just need two ear tags within 20 days of their birth. The primary and secondary ear tags both contain the same information: the Crown logo, the country code (UK), the herd mark and the calf's unique six-digit number. The only difference is that a primary tag has to be bright yellow and has big numbers that you can read from a distance. A secondary tag can be made of metal or plastic and doesn't need to be a specific size or style.

As a cattle keeper, I'm legally required to maintain a holding register which contains information about births, movements, deaths and any replacement tags that have been needed on the farm. The holding register can be a physical logbook, if you're properly old-school, but most folks just log the info onto a computer program. I've actually got an app on my phone called UNIFORM-Agri which helps keep me on track with all the info I need about my cows at the touch of a button rather than having to look it up in the office. The app also helps me when I'm filling out the Red Tractor forms with medicine records, batch numbers of drugs, movement records, finding out when a cow/calf was born and who their mother and father were. Everything, basically! I love it because it's so easy and I like really the stats and numbers side of things.

Standards that aren't legally necessary but are required if you want to be able to display the Red Tractor logo focus mainly on animal welfare, like supplying safe, suitable and legal bedding for animals, making sure animals kept outside have access to shelter and well-drained lying areas and ensuring a vet carries out an annual herd health and performance review. But there are many other areas you need to focus on, too, from hygiene requirements, like providing dedicated hand-washing and drying facilities for staff, to making sure milk-cooling systems are keeping milk at required temperatures and ensuring you have systems in place for controlling vermin. There are stipulations for storing feed, chemicals, medicines and waste safely, too. This all adds up to six and a half pages' worth of checklist.

We also have sheep and goat identification inspections, which are carried out at random by the Rural Payments Agency (RPA) to check ear tags, farm records and movement records. Fortunately, we don't have many sheep or goats, so it doesn't take long, but it's still another inspection that we have to be ready for at any moment.

OCTOBER

In October we open up the third cut and contact our feed rep/nutritionist to come to the farm so she can take a sample of it to analyse. She'll dig into the face of the clamp a bit to get a sample rather than taking it from the face itself, which wouldn't provide a good result, and fills up a small plastic bag to send off to the lab.

We do this partly because the cows are still out grazing, but the quality of the grass isn't great at this time of year, so we need to know if the third cut will work well as a buffer feed. The idea is that the silage might add a little bit of fibre into the cows' diet, so it'll travel through them slower, meaning that they'll have more energy to produce milk. More importantly, though, the third cut silo is what we give the cows as their grass feed throughout the winter. We want our cows to be eating grass both inside and out. All in all, it accounts for about 70 per cent of their diet, so we've got to make sure that they're getting the right stuff. And to ensure that, it's important to chop the third cut to the optimum length. If it's too short, it'll clump together and form cud balls, which the cows will spit out. If it's too long, they won't eat as much because they'll spend more time chewing it, but they'll be healthier because more cudding goes on, which improves rumen health. And in case parts of the last two sentences sounds completely alien to you, I'll just explain what goes on when a cow munches on some grass.

The first thing is that their teeth are very different to ours. They don't have front teeth or incisors on the top part of their jaw – they just have a hard pad. So cows don't actually grab grass with their teeth – instead, they wrap their rough tongues around a clump of it, then move their mouths in a sideways motion to saw through it with the molars on their top and bottom jaws. At this point, though, the grass isn't chewed much at all before it is swallowed – they chew it enough so it's moist and they can swallow it. Then, and I hope you're not eating right now, they bring it back up from the rumen, the largest of their four stomach compartments, into their mouth where they chew it again. Cows need these four different stomach compartments (along with the unique bacteria in the rumen) so they can properly digest grass and other plant material.

The softened food that comes back up from the rumen is called the cud. And watching a cow bring back up her cud is amazing – you can see this lump travel up from the bottom of her neck up to her mouth! It's crazy when you think about it. Cows usually sit down when they're chewing their cuds and can spend up to eight hours a day doing this. That's why it looks like cows are always eating. I remember reading that cows can chew up to around 30,000 times each day! After the grass is in small enough pieces, the cow swallows it again, where it travels back into the rumen and on into the omasum (another of the stomach compartments), which works a bit like a filter, allowing fine particles of food and fluid to move into the abomasum. The abomasum is much more like a human stomach, with acids and enzymes breaking down the food even further before it travels into the small intestine, where nutrients are absorbed.

The last of the four compartments of a cow's stomach is the reticulum, which is what traps anything the cow shouldn't have eaten, like nails, wire or anything else sharp. We do our best to pick up anything that falls off equipment we're using in the fields or in the yard, but cows have a habit of swallowing things whole. If a cow does swallow something sharp and (usually) metallic, it can inflame or even make a hole in the reticulum, which causes an infection called hardware disease. This is why farmers often give their animals a cow magnet (we do at Pembertons), which goes into the reticulum and then attracts any dangerous metal objects they swallow before they do serious damage. But even with a cow magnet, a cow can still get hardware disease, so we need to know the telltale signs to look out for, like when a cow stands with an arched back, with its head and neck extended. They also won't move very much, won't eat a lot and may grunt uncomfortably. That's one of the reasons I'm always casting an eye over the girls when I'm feeding them or moving past them – to spot signs that something isn't quite right before it turns into a big problem.

So, cudding is a good thing, partly because it tells us that they're comfortable, happy and eating well. But also, cudding means that they're producing saliva, and saliva contains a natural antacid which helps them to digest forages better. The better they digest it, the more they can eat. And the more they eat, the more milk they produce. If cows aren't chewing their cuds enough, they can end up with too much acid in their stomachs, which can disrupt the proper function of the good bacteria in their rumens. As farmers, we help them along as best we can by making sure the silage we feed them is the right quality and length.

It's pretty amazing how much good stuff there is in grass:

sugars, fibre, protein, oil, minerals and trace elements. The cell wall of grass is what provides the fibre. The rest of the nutritional composition comes from what's inside each grass cell. All of the information comes back from the lab after they've run the silage analysis. It's funny – at school, I couldn't have cared less about biology and chemistry. Now I love it!

Dad and I talk about dry matter quite a bit, and that's just the amount of material after water has been removed. You don't want anything less than about 25 per cent dry matter, because the cows won't get what they need from it no matter how much they munch through. You want dry matter to be a percentage between 30 and 50 per cent really. If it's too high, it will affect how much the cows eat, though (imagine someone just eating cream crackers and you'll get the idea). Also, if the dry matter is really low, it can lead to mould and cause the silage to heat up, which can lead to damage.

The sugar and fibre are what mainly provide energy (but you also get some from the oil and protein) and the amount of each varies a lot depending on the season. Your leafy, fresh spring grass has much more energy for the cows than the stemmy stuff you get in the autumn, although that does provide useful fibre. The amount of energy a cow takes from the feed is called metabolisable energy, which is what Dad and I are talking about when we mention 'ME'.

Like with energy, protein content is much higher in young, leafy spring grass and deteriorates later in summer. It can range from 14–28 per cent depending on the sward type, stage of growth, time of year and which fertiliser you use. For milking cows, you want a protein content of at least 14 per cent. Young stock need a bit less than that and the beefers even less (around 12 per cent).

You want the pH of the silage to be between 3.8 and 4.2, which is about the same as wine. You don't want it too high because it can cause secondary fermentation, which can cause bacteria to grow in there and lead to mould. Dad's happy with a pH of around 4.2, because the cows can eat a lot of it without getting belly ache. If the pH is a bit lower, they don't tend to eat as much. If it's less than 3 or above 5, something's gone wrong with the fermentation process. 'Ash', confusingly, is a measure of the mineral and trace element content. You want it to be around 6–8 per cent. Anything over 10 per cent tells you that the soil might be contaminated or fermentation hasn't gone as it should have.

So, when we run a silage analysis, the results have a big impact on the farm. If you're getting good results back, you won't have to rely as much on buying extra feed in to make up any deficits, which can be a big cost saving. Also, your animals will be performing much better. Back in 2017, when we had crazy floods followed by a drought in summer and the grazing wasn't good, we knew we'd have a few problems feeding cows. That was one of the reasons that, in early July that year, we bought in wholecrop. Wholecrop can be any crop in which the stalk, leaves and grain are all harvested together, but we went for winter wheat – wheat grown in the winter. Instead of being a hard grain (which is what you normally get when you harvest wheat), it's slightly softer, so it's more palatable for the cows and will give them plenty of energy. Fortunately, they were growing it at Laycock Farm, my godmother's place just up the road from us. It was the first time we'd ever bought in wholecrop while I'd been on the farm and only the second time for Dad.

When we came to harvest it – 27 acres' worth – Dad spotted a line running down the field. So I chucked my drone up and we could see clearly that one part of the field was a rich green colour and the other was a light brown. What had happened is that the year before, Laycock had split the field and put two different crops in, wheat and beans. The beans might not have made the farmer as much money, but what they do really well is hold the nitrogen in the ground, which massively helped the wholecrop on the other side of the field push on. It was a thing of beauty!

We analysed the stuff we harvested and put in the clamp and it came back as just over 33 per cent dry matter, just under 30 per cent starch, an ME of 10.2 (which was just about all right) and a protein percentage of 10 per cent. So overall, for wholecrop, that's not bad at all. We mixed it with potatoes (a really good source of energy) and a bit of meal (to add to the protein content) to create a good balance for the cows and it fed them well.

In October, in preparation for bringing the cows in for winter and bedding them up, we buy sawdust in bags by the pallet load, which arrives on an eight-wheeler. And that means I need to jump in the Manitou pronto and stick the pallet forks on. As the price of straw went through the roof a couple of years ago, we've been relying on sawdust and sawdust mixed with woodchip to bed up our young stock, seeing as it's about eight times cheaper. We still use straw for bedding up calves, though, because it's much warmer. The cows in the cubicles get bedded up with the bulk sawdust. Both sawdust and sawdust mixes do have downsides because they're a bugger to scrape and the dust is a bit of a pain, but it breaks down naturally when it reaches the slurry tank, so that's a plus. Sometimes we just have to adapt to the changing price of materials year on year.

Usually in mid to late October, but depending on the weather that year, we'll start bringing in the cows in at night. It's always a bit of a sad day, because I still remember them bouncing around with joy on turnout day back in April or May. But that's what we need to do to make sure they're well fed and looked after as the temperature starts to cool at night. We bring the high yielders back in first because they produce more milk, so they need more energy than they can get from the stemmy autumn grass on the fields. They seem to love being back inside, munching through lots and lots of grub. The low yielders are later on in their lactation, so they don't need as much energy and they're not eating as much because they're not producing as much milk (they're concentrating on making a calf). So we tend to leave them out for a wee bit longer. But if it's wet outside and there's not a lot of grass for them to munch on, the Lows make such a mess of the fields and the gateways that we bring them in too.

In October we also try and spread some slurry on the fields in preparation for winter and we need a couple of dry days to do that. In 2020, I may have taken this to the extreme by attempting to empty our million-litre (200,000-gallon) slurry lagoon using just one tractor. So, it meant early starts and getting cracking in the dark. But with the Case and the new tanker, we've got all the lights flashing away and everything looks really cool – not far off a night in Ibiza. And we smashed it – I couldn't quite believe it. What a great feeling, and what a tanker!

A lot of people ask why we can spread slurry all year round here. Well, we're not in a Nitrate Vulnerable Zone (NVZ), which is an area at risk from agricultural nitrate pollution. The danger is mainly in the autumn and winter, where the increased rainfall can carry away nutrients in the soil, including nitrogen, and pollute nearby watercourses. In NVZs, there is a closed period, from 15 October to 31 January on grassland (and 1 October to 31 January on tillage land) when you're not allowed to spread slurry at all.

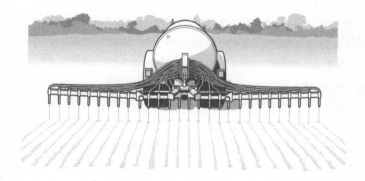

At the moment, NVZs account for about 55 per cent of the land in England, and the closest one to us is only a few miles across the Ribble estuary to the south. Like everything with the government, though, this could all change and I have a feeling we'll all be in a NVZ before we know it.

NOVEMBER

Each November we bring sheep onto the farm for the winter. They're with us until about the end of January usually and what they do really well is tidy up the fields ready for spring. They'll hoover up any weeds that have shot up, especially in areas that we might have reseeded. They'll also graze the stemmy stuff the cows won't go for, which has the combined effect of improving the quality and quantity of the grass as well as helping to maintain moisture in the soil. For the shepherd who owns the sheep, his flock are getting some grub and it means he's got fewer sheep per acre on his farm, so they'll have more grass and won't need as many feed bags. It brings in a little bit of income for us, too, so everyone's a winner. When the wintering sheep arrive, they come along with three tups (boys) to serve the ewes we've already got here. Let the tups meet the ewes! And that means in five months' time, we should see some lambs, which is great, but it also reminds me that spring is a long time away.

Sometimes we send some of our animals off to other farms for the winter as well. In 2018, 28 of our smaller heifers, aged between 15 and 18 months that had been with Mr Neptune the bull and were likely to be in calf, went to Laycock.

Wisdom from the Ginger Warrior

'The sheep poo and spread all their muck all over the field so they're recycling the nutrients all around the field, and then in the spring, we'll get some good growth.'

It should have been an easy seven cows in each load, so four round trips. But because Mr Neptune was going too, and he was an absolute a monster of a bull, weighing around 1,300kg, it didn't quite go to plan. We only just about got him in with five cows, so we had to do one more 45-minute round trip. But it all worked out well in the end because Laycock needed a bull to serve some of their heifers and Neptune was just the guy for the job. We do these kind of deals with local farms and it works well for all of us. I'd even given Mr Nep a bit of a tail and back-end trim to make him look a bit more respectable for the ladies – what a fine specimen of a bull that made him!

I went back to Laycock about a week later to worm and fluke them all. Worms and flukes are internal parasites – lovely – that can cause all sorts of problems, particularly poor appetite and feed intake. And that means the cows won't grow as well, they might lose body condition and it might have an effect on their fertility too. So it's better to stay on top of it and worm them. Prevention is better than cure and all that. After worming and fluking them, I headed to Laycock a couple of times a week to check they were doing all right, but otherwise my godmother looked after them fine over the winter.

DECEMBER

The run-up to Christmas at Birk's Farm is always exciting. Us Pembertons bloody love Christmas! The farm shop gets super busy around this time with folks making lots of orders for meat and poultry for their Christmas dinners which they pick up a couple of days before Christmas. And that means that November is always a busy month, making sure the beefers are in top condition before they end up in the farm shop. We're really proud of the meat that's born and reared on our farm and sold in the farm shop. It's about as local as you can get. It's not produced with zero road miles because we don't operate an abattoir and we choose to have our livestock picked up by the local slaughterhouse, which is only about 12km (8 miles) away. They'll come to the main part of the farm, so we have to go and move the beefers, sheep and lambs on a trailer. The pick-up always happens on a Thursday morning and then the meat will either hang there for a week or two or come back the following Monday to hang in the farm shop. It depends on how much room the butcher's got to hang the meat up here.

When you send cattle off to a licensed abattoir, you have to tell the British Cattle Movement Service (BCMS) about it within three days. It's all done online these days, but you can send them paper copies if you want. The animals must have the correct ear tags and their passports, too. It's a slightly different system for sheep and goats, but you still have to report it when you move them off your farm. You do that through a different agency – the Animal Reporting and Movement Service (ARAMS) – and need to supply information about the address the animals are moving from (here), the details of the haulier who's moving them, the address they're going to and the total number of animals. You also need to provide their unique identity numbers and make sure you register the movement within 36 hours. You can see why book-keeping is quite a fiddly job for a farmer! Fortunately, though, a lot of the information is on the UNIFORM-Agri app on my phone.

My godmother Ang sells Christmas trees from Lawns Farm and that's where Jo and I get our Christmas tree each year. Have a guess which size Jo always goes for: 5ft, 6ft, 7ft or 8ft? That's right, sports fans, it's 8ft – every time. Christmas-tree shopping tends to go the same way each year. I hold up the trees and give them a twirl, then Jo selects a couple that are put 'on standby' while we keep looking for the perfect tree. And what I mean by 'on standby' is that I guard them so no one else can choose them. Then we go back to the first of the standby trees. Sound familiar? Here's a top tip that's so obvious that I'm not putting it in a little box: don't pick up an 8ft Christmas tree in a Smart car! Then when we get home, I'm in charge of putting the string on the baubles and Jo's in charge of decorating the tree. You've got to know your place!

Turning on the Christmas lights at the farm shop is a big event in the local community around the middle of November – the RNLI came along to do it in 2019, which was an upgrade from a Mr Tom Pemberton doing it the year before. In 2019, we even constructed Santa's grotto ready for the big man himself to make an appearance and give out some presents. And you've got to have a bit of grub and booze, so we have turkey sandwiches, sausage rolls and excessive quantities of mulled wine going on (because one year we ran out). In 2019, BBC Radio Lancashire came down as well to interview us in the morning and loads of friends, family and fans of the channel pop in to say hello. It's all a bit mental, but amazing.

If you'd said that we'd be doing this a few years ago, when the farm shop was still just something that we kept mentioning wanting to do *at some point*, I'd have laughed at you. But we took the plunge, drew up the plans and even managed to get a government grant to help build it. And then, on 1 July 2017, we had the ribbon cut by no less than the High Sheriff of Lancashire, Robert Mitchel Webb (a friend of the Ginger Warrior's) at the grand opening. I was so pleased to see lots of friends, family and folks from the Lytham area there. It felt like a big moment in the history of Pembertons Farm. We've always thought of ourselves as a big part of the local community, and now we were even more so.

In December 2019, we even had two cows calve on Christmas Eve, about an hour and half apart. It was almost

a nativity scene! As for Christmas Day itself, it's still very much a working day on a dairy farm – cows still need to be fed, watered and milked and sheds need to be mucked out and scraped up, but we do everything we can on Christmas Eve just to try and make life that little bit easier on Christmas Day. We let the other guys off for the day so they can be with their family and friends. After milking in the morning, we're off to church to sing a few carols, then we drive to Jo's parents' place before I head back for a cheeky nap. Then it's off to do the afternoon milking and belt out a few Christmas classics in the parlour. I'll pick Jo up from her parents, then we'll head back to the farmhouse for Christmas dinner and, because Mum's making it, it's always absolutely banging. We do presents after dinner, after we've all had a few drinks. Works for us.

A question I get asked all the time is what do you feed your cows in winter? Well, firstly, we feed the dairy cows and the beefers the same, because it makes it easier all round if they just have one ration. We mix up the ration, which usually contains four (or sometimes five) ingredients using the Keenan feeder, to make sure that every bite is the same. The first ingredient is fodder beet, which is a bit like sugar beet but cheaper, grown in the UK in spring and harvested in late autumn. It's a high-energy and sugar-rich feed, so the cows love it. We buy in Selco, which is high in energy and protein and provides good amounts of starch and sugar. We also add a unique meal blend (biscuits, starch and so on, which comprises about 20 per cent protein). The last thing we add in is our first and second cut silage along with wholecrop silage if we're using it. We usually mix it all up in equal proportions (although we went for a 40/60 mix of wholecrop to silo when we last used wholecrop in 2017, because it's dry and full of starch and if the cows have too much they lack energy, get a bit lazy and don't want to eat the cake in the parlour). We feed them twice a day in winter after milking because it encourages them to stand up rather than lie down on the floor. This gives the teat ducts more time to close up, so they're less likely to get infections. The cows do go a bit mad for the bits of fodder beet in the feed mix and bump each other out of the way to get to it, but apart from that it all works nicely.

JANUARY

After New Year, Dad heads back out to do some slurry spreading in the shiny new tanker. We try to slurry on dry days and focus on the areas that haven't had much or any since the cows have come in. One place we don't usually get to is near the wood on the far edge of our land. It doesn't get any sun in winter because the sun doesn't come high enough and it's shielded by the trees, so the moisture stays in and the soil is always damp. But we did in January 2019 and the Ginger Warrior was thrilled about it, telling me proudly that 'the tractor didn't even make a scar'. Top job, Father. Aside from that high point, January is probably the worst month for us on the farm. It's cold, dark, usually really wet and has 31 days in it!

However, one thing does happen in January that improves everyone's mood in the farming world and beyond: LAMMA! LAMMA (which stands for Lincolnshire Agricultural Machinery Manufacturers Association, in case you were wondering) is the biggest agricultural machinery, equipment and technology show in the country and it's now held at the NEC in Birmingham. And thank the lord it is, because it used to be held at the East of England showground in Peterborough, which wasn't ideal in the middle of winter.

LAMMA is a massive event and I get proper excited, which is why it was sad to see it cancelled in 2021, but hey, there's not much you can do about a global pandemic. LAMMA is the place that you meet loads of other farmers, do business and check out the new kit that's out there. We can also arrange for demo equipment to be loaned to us for a week or a month and the sales rep will come down to the farm to show us how it works. Then we can have a think about whether we buy it, like we did with the Malone mower, which was ace.

I remember at LAMMA 2019 that the YouTube stuff suddenly felt real. My videos mainly involve just me and the Ginger Warrior and we read as many comments as we can, good, bad and indifferent. Every day's a learning day, after all. But YouTube is still a completely different world to the one where people stop you as you're walking and say, 'Hi, Tom, love the channel, mate!' It's amazing that what I mess around with on the farm and at home on the computer seems to connect to so many people, whether they're farmers or regular non-agricultural folk. I still haven't properly got used to it and can't quite understand it, if I'm honest. The first time someone came up to me and said something about the channel felt like an amazing moment. Although seeing someone come up to Dad, call him the Ginger Warrior and wish him a happy birthday was even better – the look on his face! Priceless. At LAMMA 2019, I got a bit starstruck meeting a fellow agricultural Youtuber – Gareth from Grassmen. I started asking random questions, then my mind went blank. It happens to the best of us, guys! We're so lucky to experience so much support and thanks when we're out and about and it makes an already satisfying job even better for me. But it's at places like LAMMA that I get to meet and chat to the people who are making so many good things happen for us here on the farm, and I'm so grateful for that.

For LAMMA 2020, I got a lift with my friend Hannah, the Red Shepherdess, the day before it started. Can-Am kindly put me up in a hotel for the night and we had a few drinks, which didn't help when I found myself at the NFU stand trying my hand at the drive-the-remote-controlled-car-around-the-fake-farmyard-as-quickly-as-possible game. Just to ramp up the pressure, I talked the talk beforehand, I had Hannah filming, a crowd of people suddenly turned up to watch and the top prize for the quickest time was a drone which, given my latest drone accident, would have been really useful. So... I cocked it up massively and finished last on the leaderboard. Winning! After looking at mowers, Hannah and I joined the Can-Am guys at the stand to announce the winner of their new Outlander quad bike competition. For the Can-Am LAMMA event, a huge crowd turned up and then we posed for photos with everyone and anyone who wanted one. Highlight was seeing a little kid wearing a TP hoody – great choice, son.

I'm a big fan of the Outlander – the Can-Am guys sent us one on demo which smashed it around the farm. Everyone had a go on it, including the Warrior, who loved it, and my Joanna, who got up at silly o'clock wearing her red and black gym kit to match the colours of the bike. What a lady, and I'm not sure I'd ever seen a crash helmet look so good.

The Warrior and Mother came along to LAMMA the next day – Mum doesn't usually join us, but she did this time. Dad and I aren't allowed to use the cheque book any more (!) – Mum's in charge of the finances and that's probably sensible, if I'm honest. I think it had something to do with the fact that Dad and I usually head to LAMMA just having a nosey, but that year we were properly looking at some kit with a view to maybe buying something. That was when we first started looking at things that get a lot of use on our dairy farm and needed an upgrade, like slurry tankers, mowers and a new till sower. That was Dad's top priority anyway and he made the point that if we upgraded too much of our machinery and equipment, we'd have to upgrade our tractor power too (*rubs hands together excitedly*).

Wisdom from the Ginger Warrior

'"Hi, Tom" are the words we hear most when we're wandering around LAMMA. Some people even recognise me. "It's the Ginger Warrior," I hear them whispering. It's all a bit surreal!'

FEBRUARY

Just a few weeks after LAMMA is the other big industry event for us dairy farmers: Dairy-Tech, organised by the Royal Association of Dairy Farmers, which is held at Stoneleigh Park in Warwickshire. Joanna came along in 2018 and we had a banging road trip. We had a look at the Trusti Tuber calf-feeding kit, cow brushes and Lely robots, which I'd wanted to see for ages.

The Lely robot milking system I saw was pretty amazing. Each cow has a unique barcode which is read by the robot when they're ready to be milked. If the cow's been recently milked, the robot opens the gate and the cow will know to walk out. For the ones that are ready to be milked, the machine's lasers recognise where each cow's teats are, which is super quick so the cows aren't getting stressed, then the machine cleans the teats and starts milking while dispensing food to keep the cow occupied. Plus, it recognises if one of the teats is particularly slow milking and will disconnect the other teats so the cow doesn't get overmilked, which is something that can cause a lot of damage. How amazing is that!

After each cow's used the machine, everything's cleaned and sterilised to stop cross-contamination. The system works in summer and winter and, in summer, the cows learn to head back to the machine from the fields when they're ready to be milked. The machine also recognises how much the cow is cudding and records that information to flag up if anything unusual is happening. It can also detect high cell count and can separate the milk of a cow that's been freshly calved so you can isolate the colostrum. These are massive plus points for cow health and I was hugely impressed. I also got to see the Lely Juno, an automatic feed-pushing robot that moves around the feeding alley in your shed, pushing feed towards the cows, which encourages them to eat more throughout the day and night and also saves you from having to move it around manually. Yes, it's a huge cost to begin with, but the payback over time could be incredible with the cows producing more milk.

Joanna joined me again for the drive down to Dairy-Tech in 2019, and I was massively nervous before this one because I was giving a presentation for the Dairy-Tech Innovation

Hub about Bringing Farms into the 21st Century. I did really brick it beforehand, but having Jo there smiling in the audience helped a lot. I did have a good look at cow brushes this year and a few more robots – I can't get enough of them. A few months later, GEA, an international tech company that supplies, among other things, dairy farm robots, got in touch and told me that they'd just installed their robots at a farm in Clitheroe, just 30 minutes away from us. So I contacted Shaun Hartley who owns the farm and he said he'd be happy to show me around. And wow, Shaun's place is a farm of dreams. He's got 210 milking cows going through four robots and the shed, built in 2019, is 90 metres long by 37 metres wide. It's more of an aircraft hangar than what I'd call a shed. He's got automatic GEA scrapers in as well, which work better with sand, which is what he uses to bed the cows up.

The robots wash the teats, then check for mastitis and blood, then begin milking, with a computer terminal displaying info about milking time, quantity, flow per minute and temperature. One of the amazing things this machine does is identity if a high cell count is coming from a particular teat and, if so, stop milking from that teat but keep milking the other three teats. The robot basically tells you if there's a problem with a cow long before you'd ordinarily be able to find out. Shaun told me that since they've shifted from a parlour to the robot system, they're up about 5–6 litres per cow per day. And their cell count has gone from between 250 and 300 to 120 and below. The cows all have feeding collars with barcodes which measure rumination, activity and feeding times. The system alerts you if the rumination drops and lets you know when the cows are in heat as well, so you've got an optimal time to serve them. Cow fertility at Shaun's farm had improved massively and the overall health of the herd was fantastic. His place blew my mind, basically. The only issue for me was that the cows don't graze outside, but for cows that are in all year round, it would be hard to find a healthier herd.

MARCH

In March, we start our first bit of field work for the year when the till (fertiliser) arrives. In 2020, we had a new till sower to work with. Although for some reason I decided to be really lazy and move the Manitou bucket with the pallet forks attached rather than take the pallet forks off and move the bucket on its own. Why would you do that? When something like that happens, I'm thinking, 'It's great that Dad didn't see that. Got away with it!' But then I realise I'm filming it and Dad will see the video and say, 'Tom, you're an idiot.' And now he's going to read a whole book detailing my cock-ups! Damn!

You know what, though, he's right on this occasion. To unload the fertiliser, which works out at 600kg (1,300lb) a bag, I stuck the pallet forks back on and lifted two bags at a time, one with each of the forks, and moved it into the clamp. Boom! Then, a few days later, we had some really sunny weather after a really wet spell, so I headed out in the new Case tractor with Joanna in the side seat to do some till sowing. And wow, she purred (the Case, not my Joanna). Although, with a new tractor and a new till sower, this was never going to be perfect – it was going to be all about cocking things up and learning as I do it, but that's what life's all about, isn't it? And the next morning it sure was, when I loaded up the till sower with two bags of till, but had somehow forgotten to close the dispensing chute, so we ended up with till all over the yard. Hey ho.

But on the plus side, the spreader spreads wider than the previous one and definitely spreads more evenly. Till sowing is one of those jobs that Dad always does, and I think this was the first year that he was happy for me to do some of it. Anyone who works in Ag or who has a father that they work with all the time knows that feeling – it's a big pat on the back and confidence builder. Maybe he might even let me graduate to rolling the clamp one day after the grass comes in! Not sure I did my finest work on this occasion, though – the fields were so wet, many with big pools of water, and I made a mess. But we needed to do it – the grass had started to go yellow around the damp areas, which tells me that a lot of nitrogen has come out of it and been washed away. So, with till sowing, we're putting that nitrogen back into the soil to help the grass grow. And the new till sower absolutely smashed it. We managed to get three bags of till into it at a time and 33 bags in total across let's say 200 acres (220 acres minus the massive wet patches). Now that's what I call efficiency!

Next up after the till is spreading some box muck – the straw used for the calf and young stock bedding and the manure the animals produce – as an extra fertiliser to bring about worm activity, which encourages drainage so that all the nutrients in the muck will go down into the ground and make the grass grow stronger and healthier. We usually spread box muck on the fields using the Hürlimann with a 4-tonne side-discharge muck spreader, but sometimes we hire in a 10-tonne Richard Weston one to speed things up. In 2019, we even managed to get to the top field next to the wood, which gets super wet in winter. We hadn't spread box muck there for a year or two and it didn't hurt to give the soil something with a bit of fibre in rather than wet slurry all the time. We won't mention Dad getting a bit too close to the woods and making a right mess of it. It's funny how when Dad does something like this, it never gets caught on camera, but when I do, it always does!

In 2020 we had two Case tractors to work with: the 145 Maxxum (a beast) and a 110 Farmall (with a slightly smaller spreader on it), which are both more powerful, quicker and allow you much finer control over muck spreading than the Hürlimann. So we were able to hire in two 8-tonne spreaders and smash it in a day (shout out to Steven for helping out), which wasn't bad going considering we had so much box muck in the midden that it was putting Dad in a bit of a grump. But he stuck himself in the Manitou all day to load up the two spreaders and it put him in a much cheerier mood. And when Dad's in a better mood, everyone on the farm seems to chill out! Plus, by the end of the day, we had shifted so much muck we could actually walk around the yard again.

Wisdom from the Ginger Warrior

'Slurry forces the grass but the box muck gives a bit of earthiness to the root structure and gives the worms something to work with. We've fed a lot of worms a lot of bacteria and a lot of creepy crawlies and they'll be very happy with us. All that will help build up the organic matter within the soil nicely.'

Seeing as we're in March, you know that spring is on its way, the days get longer, and it'll get drier. And that all means we're approaching one of the best times of the year for us – lambing! But there's a fair amount of prep work to do before little lambs start popping out and so we can help them hit the ground running, so to speak. Around four to six weeks before the sheep start lambing, we give them their annual booster of Heptavac. This gives them and their little ones all sorts of protection against stuff like dysentery, tetanus and pasteurellosis (a really nasty one triggered by stress which suppresses their immune systems and causes bacteria in the body to multiply massively). We bring in the sheep to vaccinate and check over them rather than do it outside. We used to have a shepherd – Francis Mercer, who's a good friend of Dad's and worked for us for about 35 years. He'd come down to the farm twice a year to take care of these sorts of things, but he retired a couple of years ago. Francis, I wish you a happy retirement and thank you so much for the work and service you put in for the Pemberton family.

But with Francis gone, I vaccinate the sheep myself and use the chance to check their feet as well, clipping anything overgrown with my pocket knife (when I'm not accidentally slicing through my hand, that is, and having to get my mum to sort me out!).

Tom's Top Tip
Now I'm no shepherd, but there's one thing I do know. Always stick your waterproofs on before handling sheep when it's been wet because their wool holds a crazy amount of moisture and you end up absolutely soaked otherwise.

In late March, we use a chain harrower attached to the Hürlimann or Case to rake up all the dead grass and move the box muck around that we spread earlier in the month. You don't want the grass to be too long at this point, or you can end up pulling it out a little bit with the harrows. But if you've timed it right, it all gives the new grass a chance to come through. In April 2019, we didn't get the timing quite right and had a surprising amount of grass underfoot that the chain harrows would have ripped out. And we definitely didn't want that, so we borrowed 3-metre spring harrows from Tom Rigby. They're better than the chains because they're more flexible and don't rip up the grass, but they do break apart the box muck we'd spread down and move it around, which helps the grass grow really well. This time of year, timing is everything when it comes to tractor work. If it's too early, you can make a mess with the tractor because the ground is too wet, and if it's too late, the grass has grown too strong and you can end up doing more harm than good.

The great things about harrowing are that you can go fast – at about 10.8 km/h (about 7 mph) – and you're also covering 3 metres at a time with the harrows, which is wider than the actual tractor, so it feels like you're getting through it quick. And you're not smashing the revs, so it's not crazy loud in the cab, which is a bonus when you're using a mic. In the areas where the fields were flooded last year, we've ended up with mossy and weedy patches which the spring harrows will rip up so we can sow new grass seeds. In the other bits, the spring harrows will go through and scratch it all up, so the grass will come through nicely in a thicker sward. Living the dream, guys! Well, that was the plan. What wasn't on the plan was crashing into a fence.

So why is Tom's farm a mess, I hear you asking? (A): cows rubbing on things, pooing and peeing on things and (B): Tom crashing into things while Snapchatting, Instagramming or YouTubing. So don't do any of these things while you're harrowing, guys – you will break fences. Learn from me!

So, lesson learned, we crack on and don't tell Father. In the end it didn't matter, because the Warrior was very happy with the spring harrows pulling out the chickweed, which stops it dominating the sward and enables the grass to overtake what remains and smother it out. And that means less spraying to do and less cost. Which equals a delighted Ginger Guy with a Moustache.

Tom's Top Tip

Anything you see on the field, whether it's bricks, broken bits of machinery or little pieces of metal, make sure you get 'em up now because you'll only hit 'em later with the mower and grass won't grow underneath that. It might only be a small thing but every blade of grass counts here!

4

LAMBING

In early April, it's lambing time and that puts a huge smile on my face. A couple of weeks before they give birth, the ewes start to 'bag up', which means their udder and teats start to grow. Closer to giving birth, the udder will get firmer and the teats get more swollen as they're filling up with milk. The ewes' behaviour also changes a bit, like heading off to a quiet corner of the field, pawing the ground with their feet, lying down, then getting up and turning around in circles and lying down again. It's all part of the nesting instinct. Then, between one and two days before lambing, the lamb will drop down inside the ewe, getting into the right position to come out. At the end of the first stage of labour, a water bag (the amniotic sac) will appear and either hangs there or bursts. If it bursts, the ewe usually starts licking it up – it's full of energy, which the girls could really do with at this point. Usually within an hour of her waters breaking, a ewe will give birth and the lamb appears front feet first, followed by its nose. It kind of looks like it's diving out. If the lamb's in the right position, the ewe doesn't need any help at all most of the time. But sometimes things don't quite go to plan and I'm there to offer a helping hand.

Back in April 2019 I did a 'Lambing Live' video featuring our friendly sheep Buttons, who'd had a bit of trouble during lambing the previous year. Buttons was Joanna's first pet lamb, and was hand-reared from a bottle. She comes up to you if you call her. She's now rather a big ewe, probably because of all the cake she steals off her pals! But this time during lambing she didn't seem to be progressing after her bag had broken, so I helped her out a bit. Of course, Toffee the Highland suddenly became very interested at this point. Not now, Toffee! Only one leg was sticking out, which isn't a great sign, so I needed to push it back and reach inside for both front feet, squeezing them together. Then the head followed and we had one healthy lamb! I had another feel inside and there was a definitely a second in there. I should mention that, before 2021, we didn't scan the ewes during pregnancy. We'd had so few ewes on the farm up to that point that it didn't seem worth it. We kind of treated it like pot luck – if they lamb, then happy days, and if they don't, they don't.

Meanwhile, Buttons was doing really well and licking the first lamb, which was a good sign. The second lamb was a big one and its head was getting stuck, so I needed to move it around a bit and guide it out. I was getting a bit stressed because it seemed to be struggling to breathe. I rubbed its belly loads, swung it by its back legs to get all the gunk out of its nose and put a bit of straw up its nose so it coughed up what was up there. Much better! Then I moved the lamb so it was next to Buttons' head so she knew that it was hers. Job done! Quite a relief. Or so I thought...

Then I started wondering if Buttons had a third lamb to come. I put the camera down to check, and before I got there a little lamb slipped out nice and easily. Damn it – should have been filming! Meanwhile, Buttons started licking the second lamb and the first one was standing up and trying to trip over its brother or sister. Five minutes after birth and already showing a cheeky side. Amazing.

Lambing was still a little bit of an unknown for me then – calves I know well, but we only have a handful of ewes and they're more pets than anything. And like pets, we probably spoil them a bit, so they might get fed slightly too much cake in the mornings. And that means they get a little bit, let's say, 'conditioned'. The trouble is, that can be a problem during lambing because you end up with a big lamb struggling to get out of a smaller than usual space because of the extra weight the mum's carrying. And that's a shepherd's nightmare.

That year, it didn't help that two of the Highland girls, Toffee and Flora, were both massively messing about trying to find out what was going on, so I had to shoo them away a couple of times. But after seeing Buttons happily licking all three of the lambs, it seemed like my work was done, so I left her to it after checking her bag. It had loads of milk inside it, so all good from here. I really hadn't expected three lambs to come out and, looking at them all afterwards, that second one was an absolute beast. Then the third one got up barely two minutes after being born – makes you realise how slow humans are! I was so pleased I was in the right place at the right time, though, and big props to my Auntie Jean, who spotted Buttons and gave me a shout to let me know that things were happening. And well done, Buttons – she's amazing!

I checked up on them the next day because the first 24 hours are the most important for lambs – after that, you know you're doing well. Unfortunately, the second one out (the beast) wasn't getting up. So I picked her up, thinking this doesn't look good, then she stretched and ran off. That's great – that's what we're after, but wow, the emotional highs and lows of lambing! Another one of the ewes had also lambed, also with triplets, which can be a bit tricky because they can only feed two lambs at once. A couple of the lambs seemed a little bit frail, so I gave them some shots of lamb boost tonic for a bit of a kickstart with energy and fibre.

In 2020, my little nephew Freddie got to see his first lamb. One of our ewes had lambed one, but I checked her and there was definitely another set of feet up there. So I helped pull it out, rubbing the belly and taking the gunk away from the nose again before bringing it round to Mum, who gave it a good lick. And then, when I checked her again, we had another one on its way, but one of its legs was bent back in utero. I just pushed it forwards so it was in the right position before pulling it out as Mum pushed. That's some good teamwork! And this is what farming is all about, bringing new life onto the farm. And then Freddie waved and said, 'Hiya' to the lambs. Nothing took the smile off my face that day. Just call me the Blonde Shepherd. (That's a gag at the Red Shepherdess's expense. Sorry, Red!)

Our last lamb that year was the smallest I'd ever seen in my life, so small in fact that I don't think he was tall enough to reach his mum's teats! So I milked the mum into a syringe (that took some time) and fed it to him by connecting the syringe to a plastic tube that goes down the lamb's throat (as with calves, make sure you go down their left-hand side because that's where the entrance to the oesophagus (food pipe) is). I do that because it's so important that lambs get some colostrum – the first milk the mum supplies, which is full of energy, nutrients and antibodies and also helps regulate body temperature and clean out the lambs' digestive systems. So it's pretty useful, basically. I also gave him some lamb boost, to give him an energy lift. I fed him some more colostrum that night, too, to make sure he'd got a belly full of milk. Fortunately, it wasn't too cold then, so we could leave them out on the field. I checked on them all the next day and fed the lamb milk from a bottle, which he chowed down with his tiny tail wagging. And I kept doing that twice a day, so we knew he was pushing on until he was big enough to get to Mum.

In 2021, Dad decided to add to the zoo that is Pembertons Farm by bringing in some Jacob sheep. Here's the Warrior:

> I've always wanted some Jacob sheep. They're so different with their unusual colour – black and white – and their two curled horns. These days, lots of people come and have a look at our farm and the animals on it and I reckon they'll love 'em – they're cute and they weren't expensive. Jacobs are unusual and that's what we're all about here. We can have them in front of the shop for people to have a look at, especially the kids. At the end of the day, we bought the Highlands to show to people, and look how that's gone (*taps FarmLife logo*)!

In case you're wondering, I did a bit of post-video research, and their name comes from the Biblical story of Jacob in the Book of Genesis. Jacob fell in love with his cousin Rachel (back when that was normal), but Rachel's dad, Laban, only gave him permission to marry her after Jacob had worked, unpaid, as a shepherd, for 14 years. Wow – seems like I had it easy with Joanna's folks! To help Jacob establish his own flock of sheep, Laban allowed him to take all the spotted and speckled sheep and breed them. That where the name comes from, anyway. Quite when Jacob sheep appeared in England is anyone's guess, although legend has it that black and white spotted sheep first arrived on a wrecked ship that belonged to the Spanish Armada in 1588. That's why they were often called 'Spanish sheep'. Since then, they've been used as ornamental sheep to graze the grass in posh parklands and stately homes to impress their visitors. And talking of posh places and impressing visitors, I think next year or the year after we'll look at having a viewing area that operates throughout the year to showcase all our animals. Watch this space. By that time, Dad will probably have bought some water buffalo or grizzly bears, knowing him.

On 24 March 2021, in preparation for lambing, Heids and I did our best sheepdog impressions to round up nine sheep from the rented fields into the trailer. We moved them to the fields close to the house – that's what we usually do close to when the ewes are due, so we can keep an eye on them. And then three days later, we had our first Jacob lambs! I probably went a bit over the top on the video, but you know me. They were triplets, too, and they all seemed about the same size, with no runt of the litter, which is amazing. It was super exciting, spring had sprung and it always feels like the best time of year when new animals are jumping about on the farm. Plus, these ones are so cute! After a really hard January and February on the farm, this makes everything feel better. And come Easter time, we moved them into the field next to the farm shop so people could see them while they were doing their shopping. And props to the Warrior, he was bang on – everyone loved them. They aren't the friendliest sheep just yet because they haven't been Pembertoned yet. When they have, they'll become the friendliest sheep in the world, and like the others, they'll come and have a munch on a bit of bread and be really happy.

When lambs are two days old, we put a small rubber ring around their tails, just where the skin finishes, using an elastrator (a pair of pliers that allows you to fix the ring in place) to dock them. If you wait any longer than two days, the lambs become so quick that they're an absolute nightmare to catch and I end up falling on my arse looking like a right nob. After you put the rubber ring on, the end of the tail beyond the ring just falls off. We do this because if you don't they get very mucky rear ends and that means come June/July, when fly season starts, you'll end up with maggot problems and, believe me, it'll be horrible. We use CLiK in summer, which is a spray-on treatment that stops larvae from developing, to be on the safe side too.

In the first 36 hours after lambing, we also do the tups' (boys') bits with the elastrator. This process works the same as the rubber ring around the tail, restricting the blood flow so anything below it just falls off. We do this to stop them from jumping on their sisters (or mum) and want to get it done as quickly and as stress-free as possible. I usually secure the lambs by placing them between my knees so they can't wriggle away. (Always keep a supply of spare rubber rings in case one pings off.) We also use the blue marker spray to give the ewes and lambs the same number so we can easily identify the members of the same family.

In 2020, not only did we have new lambs on the farm in spring, we also brought in a couple of animals that Jo suggested a while back: two baby pygmy goats! We're trying to bring more animals on the farm that are a little bit special, unusual or just really cute for visitors to see. We thought about this more and more during lockdown, turning our farm into more of an attraction for people to come and enjoy. Jo and I went on an adventure to pick them up and she even baked and packed some homemade banana bread and cookies. That's how you road trip in style, guys. Heidi is a massive fan of goats – they're her fave animal, in fact. So, as you can imagine, she was *so* pleased about the new arrivals, as were a lot of you guys who watch my videos – everybody's mad about the goats. So much so that when I shot that Sunday video about the goats, I even came prepared with a list of questions that had shown up in comments sections of my videos about them. A first for me!

Dad likes them a lot and gave them their names: Nancy (the nanny goat) and Lottie (the lady goat). We gave them the pen at the end of the calf building and bedded it up with straw to keep them nice and warm until they got a bit bigger – they were only eight weeks old when they arrived on the farm. When they first got here, they both made a high-pitched bleating noise that sounded like it belonged in a horror film despite the reassuring Heidi cuddles – maybe it was being around new people, calves and lots of other unfamiliar smells. We gave them a bit of grub and stuck in some salt licks to keep them happy and I made sure I stayed in the pen (and talked in a soft voice) for a good 20 minutes at first so they got used to me. About a week after they arrived, I was sitting in the pen feeding Lottie cut-up grapes and she'd stand on her back legs to reach a grape if I held it above her. Just call me the Goat Whisperer. Although Heids was whispering to me to tell me what to do, so I can't claim all the credit.

We won't milk them or use them for meat – they're tiny, so you're not going to get a lot of milk from them. They're here for people to come and see and enjoy. Heids has done a great job tailoring how she deals with each of them because Nancy is a bit shy, needs a bit more persuading and everything's more on her terms, so you need to let her trust you and come over to you. Meanwhile, Lottie is much more adventurous, confident, will wander over and sniff the camera and is quite happy to be picked up for a cuddle or a head scratch. That's animals for you, though. They're all different. Being able to hold Lottie meant that Heids was able to spot a lump on her right side that we got a bit worried about, so Suzy the vet came and checked it a few times. It doesn't seem to be anything serious, but it's something we'll be watching to see if anything changes. Otherwise, when Suzy checked them each over, they seemed to be doing very well and were both certainly exercising their lungs nicely.

They hadn't been hand reared so they were always going to be a bit afraid of us at first, but Heids was confident Nancy would come out of her shell soon. 'They're going to be my best friends!' she said excitedly, although I did think she was going to have her work cut out. But she smashed it as usual. Soon, Heids started to let them out into the field out the back of the shop whenever it was a nice day. If it's really cold, windy or raining a lot we tend to leave them inside, though. They go out when we're feeding the calves in the morning and we bring them back in when we feed the calves in the afternoon. They're pretty pampered pygmy goats, if I'm honest. Desmondo (my brother-in-law) even made them a seesaw that now lives in that field and we've also got them a ramp leading up to a used cable drum, which works nicely as a little table. Even the sheep are using the ramp now. This place is turning more and more into a zoo every day! Eventually, I want to build the goats a jungle gym so they can properly mess around. The kids that visit the farm will absolutely love that, I reckon. We might well breed them so we've got more running around (which is why we chose two girls), but you can only do that when they're about 18 months old, which is about now, come to think of it. That reminds me to get on with that!

We introduced Lottie and Nancy to Meghan the Highland, who wandered over to the top of the cable drum, where both the goats were standing. The drum is almost exactly the same height off the ground as Meghan's nose, and soon they all had a good sniff and a lick and seemed happy enough in each other's company. Love it.

5

CALVING

And now for the moment you guys have all been waiting for: calving! And that's probably my equal favourite time of year along with turnout day when the cows go out to grass in late April. The cows calve through the year, which means that the amount of milk we produce through the year stays the same. But we do tend to have some calves each spring.

For the heifers (cows that haven't calved yet), calves are calved the old-fashioned way. And that means we move the cows who we're looking to get in calf and then the bull goes about his business. From 2017 to summer 2021, that was Mr Neptune, who did an absolutely cracking job for us. But after he went lame and broke his shoulder, we made the sad decision for him to leave the farm. We had to get ourselves a new bull soon, though, to get the girls in calf so we keep up producing beef for the farm shop.

Back in autumn 2017, just a month after the farm shop opened, we decided we wanted to bring an Angus bull onto the farm with a view to selling more beef. Anguses are well known for the amount of fat that builds up within their muscles. This is what makes meat marble, which is what gives you the flavour and succulence. We're a grass-fed farm, which suits Anguses, because they don't need a lot of cereals to eat, which are also relatively expensive to bring in. An Angus bull's temperament is a lot better than, say, an Ayrshire's. Our last Ayrshire bull (Lloyd, named after one of our lads who used to milk cows at the weekend) knocked the Ginger Guy into the feed trough, so we were keen to avoid that happening again! Another reason we chose an Angus bull is that their calves come out really easily, which is good for the calf but also means the heifers can join the milking herd sooner.

So on a recommendation we went up to Angus breeder David Wellock and his partner Wendy in Otterburn, North Yorkshire, to select a bull. David had two for us to choose from and they were both 16 months old. When looking at a bull, you should always check out their calves and heifers to get an idea of what you can expect from your own calves. Neptune was a bit shorter-legged than the other one, which might mean he stays short in stature and that's useful because his main job on our farm is getting on the young heifers. He also had a bigger back end, which is where your more expensive cuts of meat, like fillet and sirloin steaks, come from, so that's why we went for him.

Because Neptune had been such a massive legend while he was with us, Dad and I went up to Dave and Wendy again to find a new bull in August 2021. We had a look at five different bulls this time. Two of them seemed to be the front runners – Boris and Nigel. They came over when Dave banged the feed trough and seemed quite friendly sorts with good temperaments. I always look for a nice round back end (wahey!) and Nigel was a bit smaller than Boris, the right sort of size for our heifers. Sometimes there are just little hard-to-describe differences that lead you to choose one over the other. It might be if they come to the feed rail first, their confidence, the way they walk or how they hold their feet. You start thinking ahead and wondering if they might end up with foot issues, that sort of thing. So in the end we chose Nigel, who we then found out was actually Neptune's cousin. Nige is coming to Pem's! And family-wise, Nige comes from a 200-year-old line of Anguses, which is some serious pedigree.

A couple of weeks later, Wendy and David drove big Nige down to the farm. And seeing as it was a Friday, we got some ladies together from the rented fields over the road to welcome him to Pem's. He's been TB'd before he came down so he was all good to go and the ladies seemed well interested (actually one of them was so interested that she even showed Nige how to get the job done). All the cows that he serves will give birth to Angus calves, which we'll sell in the farm shop. It's all about from farm to shop and as few road miles as you can manage!

For the dairy cows, though, everything's done via AI (artificial insemination). We use AI for them because we can improve the overall herd at a fraction of the cost and not need another bull. A bull is fantastic at getting cows in calf,

> **Wisdom from the Ginger Warrior**
> 'If you buy a bull that's been halfway up a hill on
> not as good ground as we've got, and if they do well
> up there with the longer winters and the rougher
> available grazing, they're going to do nicely on the
> Fylde coast.'

but you are limited to how much he can do. If there are six cows on heat, he'll struggle to cover them all before they come off heat. But the main reason is that you can never be better than the bull you own. If there's a problem with your bull, you can't change things up quickly. But if you're using AI, you can change straws pretty fast and go on to the next bull. Also, different cows might need to improve on different things and AI allows you to do that. For example, a cow that doesn't give loads of milk will need a bull that will improve milk volume. And a cow that gives loads of milk but needs a bit more condition will need a chunkier bull. And reason number three, for a bonus, is that when you use AI, you can choose sexed semen straws, which gives you an up to 97 per cent chance of having a heifer calf rather than a bull calf. Any dairy bull calves born on the farm we sell on to other farms.

AI involves me with a big plastic glove 'serving' the cows when they're in heat, which happens every 21 days. We buy in 'straws', plastic vials of bull semen (diluted in egg white), which are frozen using liquid nitrogen. They're deposited into the cow's uterus using a specialised AI gun which works a bit like a plunger.

So the first thing you do is thaw the straws in warm water (around 37.5°C/99.5°F) so they're ready to use. Then you need to place one inside the AI gun, which deposits the semen in the right place when the time comes, and press the plunger to prime it. Now you get the cows nice and calmly into a stall (we use the ones opposite the nursing pens next to the parlour) and chained at the back to secure them. Next, you cut the sealed end of the straw at a 90-degree angle and then secure the gun inside your overalls to maintain the right temperature. Put an arm-length plastic glove on your left hand (if you're right-handed) and squirt some lube onto your hand and fingers. I'm going to insert this hand into the cow's rear end to clear out any excess manure. Then, I clean the vulva to stop any contamination and with my right hand I'm going to reach inside and feel for the cervix before inserting the gun. Once the gun is through the cervix, you'll feel some resistance, and that's when you know to deposit the contents of the straw slowly using the plunger. This only takes a few seconds, and that's it – job's a good 'un.

Tom's Top Tip

I find that warming the AI gun by rubbing it between my hands is the right way to go to make sure things run smoothly. It's important the cows are as relaxed as possible!

So why is it important we get our cows in calf? It's to keep up their milk output. Cows only produce milk after they've given birth – like humans, you see. And also like humans, they're pregnant for nine months. Here, we serve them for the first time when they're between 14 and 15 months old, so they're giving birth to their first calf when they're just over two years old.

About four weeks post-service, one of the vets at Oakhill comes to scan the cows using an ultrasound scanner to see if they're in calf. We call it in PD'ing – pregnancy detection. They feed the scanner via a tube into their rear ends so it sits over the uterus. They have these fancy goggles that enable them to see what they're looking at, but we can see what's happening on a portable screen that shows us the same image. At the four-week point, we can hear the heartbeat, check if everything's looking OK and see how many calves are in there. It always makes me smile when we've got a cow in calf, particularly if it's one of my favourite girls. I don't think that feeling will ever change!

The vet also uses the ultrasound scanner to check any cows that have been struggling to get in calf, so we can find out if there are any problems that we can fix. They'll also check any cows that have calved in the past few weeks to make sure that they're healthy and haven't developed any problems or infections. If they're OK, then I can serve them again and the cycle continues.

The cows have a couple more check-ups from the vet while they're in calf to see that everything's moving ahead normally. After that, the next major milestone is the drying-off period, for those cows who have had calves before. It's called the drying-off period because we stop milking them in this time. In the weeks beforehand, we'll start reducing their feed intake so they're not producing high volumes of milk. At the point of drying off, we move the cows to another field (along with the other dry cows) to rest and chill out. Nothing but the best treatment at Pembertons! First-time calvers, who haven't started to produce milk yet, don't get the same VIP treatment, but their time will come.

The drying-off period is a really important time for quite a few reasons. In the first week after drying off begins, the risk of developing new udder infections is at its highest – approximately 60 per cent of early lactation mastitis begins in the dry period. This is why we usually give the girls a course of antibiotics to get rid of any infections and stop new ones from taking hold. Meanwhile, during this first week after drying off, the udder starts forming its natural defence mechanism in the teat canal – a keratin plug, a wax-like substance that seals the canal so any nasty bacteria can't make their way up there.

One thing that can interrupt the keratin plug forming properly is if the cow has any residual milk hanging around in the udder at the point of drying off. If there is milk left in the udders, it can divert the cow's white blood cells from doing what they should be doing at this point – helping to stop bacteria entering the udder. A high milk volume still in the udder can also lead to a less effective keratin plug forming.

If everything goes as it should, though, the keratin plug remains in place before disappearing in the week before calving, when the udders are going to be called upon a lot. We've started to make a change over the last few years where we put a sealant in the base of the cow's teats to make sure we get a really good plug. We are also looking at using fewer antibiotics each year and just using the sealant without antibiotics for cows with low cell counts (i.e. for those in better health).

Like with the pregnant ewes, pregnant cows 'bag up' around two weeks before they calve (but it can sometimes be a lot closer to calving than that), which means their udders drop down and start to swell with the first milk for their little ones. They might also start to leak a little bit of milk. Other signs that a calf is on its way soon are that they'll lift their tails up and start behaving a bit unusually. Like lying down, then standing up, lying down and standing up. Or heading into corners of the field to get away from other cows. Also their pelvic bones, on either side of their tails, will drop because the ligaments surrounding their pelvis relax.

The majority of the time, cows calve without any problems and once things kick off, it can all be over as quickly as five minutes. First, they'll usually lie down in the corner of a field, then start straining and pushing, which means the uterus is contracting and the calf is moving into the birth canal. Sometimes, the cow's water bag (which helps loosen the birthing canal) will appear out of the vulva, break and fluid will rush out. Next comes the second bag – the amniotic sac, which surrounds the calf. Soon the calf's feet should be visible (hooves pointing downwards) through the sac, followed quickly by the head. As with the lambs, we basically like the calves to come out in a diving action! Once the shoulders are out, things tend to move quickly. The umbilical cord breaks and the calf begins to breathe on its own. Soon, Mum will start licking it all over, which looks cute, but more importantly helps stimulate blood flow and stops the calf from getting chilly. Within the next few hours, the cow will pass the placenta (also called cleansing).

Back in September 2019 when number 132, who's one of my favourite cows, was calving, we had to be a little bit careful because she was a fifth calver, therefore much more likely to develop milk fever (which I talked a bit about in Chapter 2). I got her in the cow crush and gave her a bolus down the throat with the bolus gun, which gets the pellet far enough down to make sure she swallows it. Then we moved her back to the nice comfy nursery pen. By the next morning, though, something very exciting had happened. We had a Charolais calf! And Mum had drunk lots of water and had a good bite to eat. Boom! I just needed to get another bolus down her to ward off milk fever, spray the calf's navel to make sure it dried up nicely and get some colostrum into the calf using a tube, which Heids did, no bother. Heids named him Charlie and spent her lunchtimes in the pen with him.

The Highlands are always a bit special and July 2017 was a big month for us when our first Highland calves – Flora and Toffee – were born on the farm. Just so we've got the family tree for the Highlands sorted, the first two to arrive were Harriet and Minnie back in 2015. In 2016, they were ready to have calves for the first time, so we sent them off to Robert and Wendy Phillip of Hellifield Highlanders to get served by a bull. And in 2017, we hired Singleton from Robert and Wendy to come down for a couple of months' holiday on the sunny Fylde coast. What a life, eh!

Fitting their ear tags was a bit of a nightmare, though, because I'd waited far too long to do it, so by the time we got round to it, they were super quick and pretty chunky. Plus, you've got two pissed-off mums – Minnie and Harriet – following you around with some massive horns. First we went for the old tried and tested *distract the mums with some grub* approach so we could shepherd Flora and Toffee into a makeshift pen, but that didn't work. They just took mouthfuls of grub with them and disappeared off to the far corner of the field with their calves. Then I got a reinforcement in the form of Des, my brother-in-law. After seven unsuccessful attempts, we managed to get one of them (Toffee) into the pen and attach a halter (basically two loops of rope, one of which has a free end so you can lead the animal where you want it. It's a safer way to do anything with stock, if you can grab them!). Then we fixed the ear tags with their name and number on.

Flora was even trickier and managed to slip out of my rugby tackle. The video I made during all this was beginning to look like a comedy sketch. Finally, I got a halter around Flora near the gate and led her over to the makeshift pen to put the tags in. Phew! We all learned something that day: don't wait to tag Highland calves while you let other people come up with name suggestions for them. Tag them as soon as possible after birth, unless you want to spend your morning sprinting up and down, sliding around and being dumped on your arse repeatedly. And if the England rugby team's defence coach ever needs a new idea for tackling practice, give me a ring! If you can catch a two-week-old Highland calf, you can catch a New Zealand winger. Believe me!

The following spring, Harriet had another calf, born on 22 May 2018 (Jo called the date, so props to her). Dad decided to call her Meghan, after the Royal Wedding, which had been just three days earlier. Meghan was up and about after an hour, helping herself to her mum's colostrum, which, as I've said before, is so important because it's full of antibodies that will help protect her against bacteria and viruses. I was a year older and a year wiser after last year's ear-tagging shocker, so I had the tags ready to go on the day she was born. No chasing calves through fields for this guy, just a quick clip here and there. Lesson learned, job done.

Minnie gave birth nearly two weeks later, on 2 June 2018. One of the milkmen saw her licking the calf just after 5.30 in the morning and gave us the heads-up. Dad and my uncle Mike chose the name Kate to keep up the royal theme. Minnie was looking after her fine, licking her all over. They were both very comfortable with me being right next to them, which was amazing. Minnie was even happy enough to wander off and have a munch on some grass, leaving me to babysit. That's all because I feed Minnie every day and she knows me well, but it wouldn't work if anyone else was in here, because she'd get very protective of her calf and quite probably very upset.

On 18 May 2019, Minnie had her third calf, this one a heifer. We put out the naming duties to Facebook and Instagram and you came up with May. What more can you say? Perfect, born in May and goes nicely with mum Minnie. Once again, I left it a bit too late to put the ear tags in, and by the time I'd got to her, she was quick as anything. This time, the old *distract the mum with cake* approach did work. Well, for about ten seconds. Then I resorted to the rugby tackle, picked her up gently and carried her back over to where Dad was with the tags (and the camera). And that was that. I also took the opportunity, seeing as it was right before 10am on a Sunday, just before the farm shop opened, to move the Highlands over to the paddock opposite to the shop so people can see them while they're doing their shopping. When moving the Highlands (who have got really used to the sound of a bag of cake rustling), all you have to do is open the gate, walk along the gravel path to the gate to the other paddock and shake the bag. They'll all follow you, even May, who trotted after her mum, no bother. I feel a bit like the Pied Piper sometimes on this farm, you know. Don't even need to look behind me sometimes. I used a quick trick that my sister Penny suggested, filling up hay nets (she uses similar ones for her horses, but with smaller holes) and tying them up to the trough opposite the shop. That way, the

Highlands don't eat as fast as they would if you stuck some feed in a trough, so it keeps them looking pretty and facing the customers for longer. I love it when I see people taking photos of our animals and kids pointing and getting excited.

Tom's Top Tip
Always carry a length of string in your pocket or in the tractor cab. Everyone working on a farm needs a technical piece of string that'll do a job if you need it to!

On 4 June 2019, Dad said to me in passing on the farm, 'I see we've got a boy!' I shouted, 'You what?' and then got on with my morning jobs. Each day over the previous two weeks, I had been confidently saying that this was the day that Harriet would have her calf and been completely wrong. So it didn't even occur to me that Dad was talking about the Highlands. And then I did a double take when I walked over to the Highland paddock. We've got a boy! Our first Highland boy born on the farm. So proud. Dad wanted to call him Junior, so that's what we went with. We figured he must have been born the previous night because he was quite dry. The next day, I must have done something right, because I gave the Highland mums some cake, slowly walked over to Junior, who didn't run away, and helped him towards the ear tags I'd put on the fence. Didn't even need to pick him up. Smashed it at last. Harriet even stopped bawling and wandered away to graze. Maybe I'm finally learning something.

In August 2019, Moretti the seven-year-old Highland bull arrived from Hellifield, who Dad perfectly described as 'a ginger bull with two bloody big horns'. Maybe he'd found a kindred spirit. And yes, I think Moretti had been named after the Italian beer, in case you're wondering. Moretti's job was to get Harriet and Minnie in calf again and for Toffee and Flora to get in calf for the first time. At that point, they'd just turned two and it was the first time they'd been introduced to a Highland bull. First thing we needed to do, though, was play musical Highlands to get everyone in the right places. So we moved Meghan and Kate who, at just over a year old, were too young to see the bull. That was the first time we'd got them into a trailer, and all things considered (i.e. no one got stabbed by horns or ran down Ballam Road), it went pretty well. We shifted Meghan and Kate over to the paddock in front of the house before moving them to the paddock in front of the shop a couple of days later (when the weather was better and they wouldn't ruin the field). Next we moved Harriet, Minnie, May and Junior into the field next to the horse paddock. Flora and Toffee (Harriet and Minnie's first calves) were already in that field, and they had been bossing Meghan and Kate around for ages. So when Harriet and Minnie turned up, Flora and Toffee tried to give their mums the same treatment, but they were having none of it. And that's how the Highland hierarchy sorts itself out – a quick locking of horns and a realisation that you've bitten off more than you can chew!

Getting Moretti into the field was a bit of a squeeze,

particularly along the alleyway between the two containers on the way to the viewing gallery. He was a properly big lad! But he settled in well and seemed pretty chilled with me being in the field with him and his new ladies. He wasn't following them around madly, so I don't think any of them were in heat. Normally, for the past couple of years anyway, the bull's gone for one of the Highland girls straight away, but hopefully he cracks on soon. He left the farm in November after a three-month holiday, the day that BBC Northwest showed up to film a segment on my life as a YouTube farmer. Naturally, it all went perfectly to plan. And by that I mean, Moretti didn't go into the trailer first time, we didn't have one of the Highland girls trying to hurdle a fence and Moretti didn't knock the controller to my drone off the fence post that I stuck it on! But he was in on the second attempt after Father and I moved slowly towards him holding either end of a detached gate to gently shepherd him back towards the trailer while also protecting us a bit in case he chose to move towards us with his big-ass scary horns. And we'll take that, thank you very much.

Tom's Top Tip

The second a bull who's normally placid suddenly turns his head when you're trying to move him towards a trailer, get out of his way and let him have a run around before attempting to manoeuvre him again.

Unfortunately, though, when we PD'd the Highland girls a couple of months later, we didn't get the news we were after. Most of the time, when Andy or one of the other vets comes round to scan the calves, I'm a very happy farmer, but this time, it was really hard to take. First up on the scanner was Toffee, and I know you're not supposed to have a favourite, but she's mine, but no calf. And then Flora, too, followed by Harriet and Minnie. I was absolutely gutted, because I was hoping for all four to be in calf. We weren't sure what the problem was, though in fairness I'd not seen Moretti jump on any of the girls while he was here. But I suppose these things happen and in the end, it didn't matter quite as much as it would, because in the first year of COVID no one could come to the shop and see the Highlands anyway. It didn't stop it from being a real blow, though. It was the first time in my farming career that I'd used a bull and none of the cows/ heifers he'd been with were in calf. So always check and see how your cows and bulls are doing and make sure you have regular vet appointments.

On 28 March 2021, Heidi rang me first thing in the morning, and when she does that, something's broken, something won't work or something's happened with the cows. But this time it wasn't something bad. Heids sounded excited and that was because Minnie had just had a new Highland calf and it was cuter than cute. We'd been waiting two years for a Highland calf after the disappointment of Andy's PD visit, so this was great news. And this calf was extra special because it was our first Angus/Highland cross after we decided to let Neptune serve the Highlands back in the summer of 2020. We knew Mr Nep had good swimmers because, well, we had loads of his calves about, but you never quite know how something's going to go. But in the end, everything went to plan and the birth all happened without a problem. I couldn't have been happier! It's mental that in the space of 12 hours, you've got a clean, dry calf standing up and running around like it's been on the farm for weeks. I didn't get too close – I wanted to leave them to it – but I think this probably counted as the best Sunday video ever (even though we'd been TB'ing on the same day, so that's saying something). We did a shout out for names for the new calf on the Facebook page, although (just for the record), I was massively pushing for Jupiter. In the end, though, we went for Pluto, which was so popular that maybe 40 people suggested it. We loved it because the name worked so well – the mum's Minnie, named after a Disney character, and the dad's Neptune, a planet (and also a Disney character!)

The next morning, we tagged his ears (nice and easy this time!) and put the rubber band around his nuts, which doesn't hurt and just makes them go numb before they fall off in a week or two. Then we let him go slowly and gently. He seemed to be doing just fine – he didn't even go for a drink off Mum, which they usually do if they're feeling a bit stressed. Minnie was making a bit of a racket throughout the tagging, but you can't blame her for that. She's relaying two lots of information at the same time – calling to warn me that she's here and letting her calf know that's she's there for him.

And because everyone had been so good (and probably because I love the Highlands so much), I brought along a cake bag, only it hadn't got cake in it. It had something even better (well, to cows anyway): bread. The perfect thing for helping Minnie forgive me after tagging her calf up. So why had we randomly got a bag full of bread? Well, we deliver milk to a care home and they have lots of bread going. They watch the channel and know that we'll feed it to the Highlands, so they kindly load us up. Thanks a million, guys. Standing there, feeding the Highlands bread, made me wonder about starting up Tom's Farm Tours for kids, feeding the Highlands, watching us milk the dairy cows and having a go putting the teat cups on. We've already got public viewing areas, picnic tables and a farm shop, so it makes sense. Watch this space!

Just a couple of weeks after little Pluto was born, on 14 April 2021, we had some other hugely exciting news. I was driving past the Highlands on the Case with the camera on and standing next to Harriet was another calf! Love it when that happens, but can't believe I missed it again. This one was another boy, so we tagged him up and put the band around his nuts. I was still keen on the name Jupiter, but Heids suggested Mars and, thinking about it, I preferred that, so that's what we went with. I also put Pluto's nametag on – he was two weeks old and a little tricky to catch, but we got there. Mars was hiding behind his mum a bit, but I knew he would like me a lot more in a couple of weeks when I gave him a bit of cake. Then he'd know that I'm a super-cool guy.

Sometimes, though, things don't go to plan during calving. Early in 2021, two dairy calves were born prematurely. One we kept warm by bringing it in front of the Aga in my mum and dad's kitchen. We put a coat on it, too, to keep it toasty and it seemed to be pushing on, but it died in the night, which really hit me hard (and my mum, who had been a trouper throughout) because I'd been so excited to see it in the morning and we'd tried so hard to give it a fighting chance. As a family, we've always been like that. I remember coming into the farmhouse as a kid loads of times and seeing Mother and Father warming up very young or sick calves and lambs by the Aga in the kitchen. We go the extra mile for our animals.

The other calf was born about a week later and was 19 days early. The mum was showing no signs of bagging up when we put her through the footbath earlier that day, so it was a big surprise. I was worried, though – the calf was really small and I feared the same thing would happen, so I had everything crossed for her. I surrounded her with lots of straw to warm her up a bit, but what I really needed were some heat lamps. Then I got lucky – our next-door neighbour had two, but I had no idea how high they should be. Then I got lucky again – I was just about to have a Zoom call with some fellow farmers, so I took the opportunity to ask for some advice. Two of the folks – Stella and Phil – told me the lamps should be about 60cm (2ft) above the calf. I also learned that you don't want them too low because that can dehydrate the calf, which can be really dangerous, particularly when they're this vulnerable.

So while I was saying thank you to the kind folks on the webinar, I was also frantically texting Heids, who was with the calf, to move the heat lamps. It was all go, but I'm fortunate to have such a fantastic team behind me here. Also, for any young farmers out there, don't be afraid to ask questions. It's so much better to ask what might seem like a stupid question than make a stupid mistake. And if you do make a stupid mistake, that's OK, but own it and learn from it.

> **Tom's Top Tip**
> Always have colostrum in the freezer in case you have a problem with a calf and you need to access some ASAP! It's the most important thing in the world for calves and after a premature birth you might not get any from the mum.

When I got back to the nursing pens, the calf had only gone and moved away from the heat lamps that Heids had just moved and started playing in the straw, but it was a great sign that she was up and about. I moved the lamps up a little bit more so she wouldn't hit them if she got up. The calf's mum was lying down on the other side of the gate, just a couple of feet away, and was making some encouraging noises. Next thing to do was to get the defrosting colostrum into the calf as soon as we could, so she could start warming up from the inside out as well as from the outside in. I took a big risk heading into Mum's kitchen wearing my mucky dungarees, but she wasn't there and I figured she couldn't shout at me two weeks later when the video came out!

I heated the colostrum to about 37°C (98.5°F) in a milk bottle and then attached a tube because I was pretty sure she wouldn't take the milk from the bottle. So, I inserted the tube down the left-hand side of her mouth, nice and easy, don't force it, just pull and push, and then elevated the milk so gravity could do its work and 2 litres (3½pt) of milk found its way into her belly. This is great nourishment for the calf, but it also means they'll warm up from the inside out. And soon the calf started to try and get up, which is exactly what I wanted to see.

Both of the calves' mothers (31 and 22) were second calvers and they'd both been served with Ayrshire sexed semen from the same bull, so it seemed like too much of a coincidence that they were both born prematurely. Suzy from Oakhill vets was coming over the next day for a routine visit, so I let her know what was going on and we agreed we'd need to get some blood tests done pronto. I did worry that it might be neospora, a parasite that can affect cattle and cause serious problems in pregnancy.

We put a coat on the calf early in the evening (on its smallest setting and it was still baggy, which gives you some idea of how tiny the calf was) and gave her another litre of colostrum. Calves usually take 4 litres of colostrum, but she wasn't a big calf and had a belly full, so I didn't want to overdo it. I asked Dad to check up on her before he went to bed and let me know and all seemed well. I came in to see her at 6am the next day and she looked pretty good – nice and toasty in her coat. So happy! Suzy arrived a bit later and checked her for an enlarged thyroid gland (which she told me can happen due to a deficiency in iodine) and gave her a once-over to make sure she didn't have a fever or any other evidence of infections. Suzy thought she might have a bit of acidosis (too much acid in the blood) and suggested giving her electrolytes in 2 litres of warm water to get her hydrated and perk her up, which we did. And then I gave her a little helping hand to put her on her feet. And she was up! Although she did somehow manage to get poo in her ear and then somehow remove her coat. By the end of the day, we moved her in with another calf and she was messing around, which was great to see.

The next morning, she'd made it to the three-day mark and was through the worst of it. So we named her Lou and tagged her up. Honestly, one of the best parts of farming is when something goes wrong and you work really hard to make it right and it comes good. It was a team effort and I wouldn't have been able to do it without Heidi, who worked so hard at all hours to give Lou the best chance she could. We also heard that neither of the cows with premature calves had tested positive for neospora, so while we couldn't find a reason for the weird coincidence, we had a happy, healthy calf, which was the most important thing.

If you're wondering, we named her after Louise Hartley, who tragically died in 2016 aged just 24 from a rare form of ovarian cancer. She was the daughter of a Lancashire dairy farmer and had worked at the *Farmers Guardian* since 2013. The Louise Hartley Foundation was set up to honour her memory, offering scholarships to help young people get into farming, and I was on a Zoom call with members of the foundation when we were trying to save our premature calf. So a big thank you to a very worthy cause.

A couple of weeks after Lou was born, we had to call in Oakhill again because we had a heifer (number 64) who was having problems calving that I couldn't sort. She'd been in a calving box overnight and at 6pm the next day I put my hand in and everything seemed OK – the calf was in the amniotic sac and in the right position. At 9am, the feet were coming out, so I gave them a pull to help her along, but the calf wouldn't budge. And it was the hardest I'd ever pulled a calf before. I rang Dad and he told me to ring Oakhill. Charlie from Oakhill arrived, did an exam and thankfully the calf was alive and not in distress. He told us the cow's cervix was quite tight, so we could either give her an epidural and try and get the calf out or we could do a C-section and go in the side. We went for the latter because we didn't want to waste more time on something that might not work. Instead of waiting for another vet from Oakhill to help out, Heids put her hand up and volunteered straight away to scrub in, so it was definitely a learning day for her! In fact, seeing as we'd only had two or three Caesareans since I'd been here, it was a learning day for us all.

First, Charlie felt along the cow's vertebrae to locate the place that he'd need to put in the spinal block to numb the area so the cow wouldn't feel anything. Then he shaved the cow at the point he'd need to insert the needle for the spinal block (which is a big needle). But before he did that, he injected her with a smaller needle to give her some local anaesthetic, which meant that when he put the big needle in for the spinal block, she wouldn't feel that. Cow comfort comes first! Poor girl was still contracting, but her cervix just wasn't opening. So Charlie injected her uterus with a muscle relaxant, which makes manipulating the uterus much easier, and then some Metacam under the skin which helps with pain relief after Charlie's finished operating.

Then Charlie cleaned the area with some hibiscrub and surgical spirit, which is about the best you can do outside of a hospital to make everything as clean as possible. Next he went in with a scalpel, and it always amazes me how many layers you need to get through. Then it was my turn as Charlie's glamorous assistant to grab the calf by the feet and pull her out while Charlie extended the opening, checked to see if there was another calf in there and started examining the uterus. Meanwhile, I put a piece of straw up the calf's nose to clear out some of the gunk and help her take her first breaths. Then I found out something I didn't know (thanks, Charlie!), which was to fold the calf's front legs underneath her torso to help open up her airways (imagine a calf in a pose you'd expect a frog to be in). And we had a living, breathing calf! We named her Clemmie, because that's the name of Charlie's girlfriend, because that's the kind of thing we do here.

Then Charlie flushed the mother's insides out with a salt solution and got to work stitching her back up, leaving one suture at the bottom untied in case she developed an infection, which can happen, and we needed to drain any nasty stuff without having to undo the sutures ourselves. And what a tidy job Charlie did. Lastly, Heids sprayed the wound with silver spray to help minimise infection and Charlie injected the cow with antibiotics to reduce the risk of post-operative complications. And I milked the cow so we could get the colostrum into the calf as soon as poss, which I did with the tube down the left-hand side of her throat, as we did with Lou a couple of weeks before. She chowed down 3 litres (5pt), which was amazing. Mum and calf seemed to be doing well, Oakhill smashed it as usual and Heids got her hands in for the first time, so it was a massive team effort and job's a good 'un.

The next day, the new mother – number 64 – was up and alert, which was great. Meanwhile, Clemmie was already making friends and had squeezed through to the pen next door with Lou and the other calves. We gave number 64 some cake, which she ate, and milked her in the parlour, but all her milk went into the dump bucket because we didn't want any of the painkillers or antibiotics getting into our bulk tank. We stuck two red bands on her tail so it was absolutely clear in case someone else milked her. But just as things were looking up, a pregnant fourth calver was having some problems during labour and when I put my hands in, it felt like her uterus was twisted. This was another cow who we'd AI'd with semen from the same bull as with the two heifers who had given birth prematurely. I called Oakhill and within half an hour (!) they sent Sam, who managed to turn the calf around inside the uterus and deliver a healthy calf. I couldn't believe the run of bad luck we were having, though, having to call Oakhill out twice in two days.

And then, after posting my video of the premature calf, a farmer got in touch from Warwickshire asking if we'd been using semen from one particular bull. It turned out that he'd had problems delivering three calves that had all been conceived using the same bull too. It was useful to find out this info, but it didn't help solve our worries, because we had another 20 cows in calf to this bull on the farm. So we made sure we watched them closely and were ready for any issues around birthing. Luckily they all calved fine, but we didn't use semen from this bull again, just to be on the safe side.

> **Tom's Top Tip**
> After a cow has calved, fill up two buckets of warm water and let her drink them down. The water fills the rumen up and makes her eat more to keep her strength up.

In late July 2021, Meghan gave birth to a little boy, who we called Bruno (and it's just a weird coincidence that we now have a Bruno and a Mars). It happened when I was away in Ireland filming, unfortunately, so I couldn't film it, but it turned out to be a bit of a tricky one. Dad and Luke, one of our milkers, had to use the calving jacks – the first time we've had to use them on the Highlands – because the wee calf had got himself into a backwards position, but it all worked OK in the end and he's a happy, healthy calf. You have to love that I was in Ireland with all these TV cameras here, there and everywhere and my phone was buzzing every five minutes with a live feed of what was happening back home. I wouldn't have it any other way!

And then, just a couple of weeks later, Kate, one of our Highland girls (daughter of Minnie and born in 2018, in case you don't remember), bagged up and soon the water bag was dangling out, so we knew we were in business. It was her first calf, but she lay down with her back end against the fence, which wasn't going to work when a calf needed to come out, so I got her up and she moved over next to the hedge. I was really excited because I was on the farm when a Highland was actually calving! In the past the Highlands had always calved in the night on their own, so the first you know about it, you go into work and you see a new face looking at you. Mum, Dad and I had a cup of tea while we waited, but after about an hour and a quarter, Kate seemed to be struggling a bit, so I went over to have a look before moving her to a makeshift paddock and putting a halter around her so we could see what was going on. This doesn't normally happen for Highlands – they usually calve by themselves, no bother.

I could feel two legs, so everything was in the right place, but the calf didn't seem to be coming, so we attached ropes to each of the hind legs and used a calving jack, which cranks the calf slowly through the birthing canal. You must always pull when the mum pushes. Soon the head came out, then the shoulders, and the calf was alive and breathing, so all good. I told Dad to remove Kate's halter to make her a bit more comfortable and left her to it to let her bond with her calf. Kate starting licking the calf all over, which is always sweet to watch, but then I must have got too close with the camera because she moved over towards me and butted me with her head before moving back. I took that as my cue to leave the field, but in all honesty, I was lucky that she stopped when she did. It was clearly a traumatic calving for her and it was my fault for being too complacent. Kate's not as friendly as Harriet and Minnie are – the older Highlands who have calved a few times already – and I made a mistake being that close. I kept it in the video because I always want to show what happens on our farm, good or bad. Too many accidents happen on farms and this could have been a lot worse than it was, so if someone else learns from my mistakes, that's a small price to pay. I'll certainly learn from it in the future.

The next morning, I tagged up the little guy, who we'd called Jupiter, to keep up the planet theme that we've got going on. I also did his nuts because we don't want bulls when we've got so many of his sisters around. It's amazing how quickly cows and calves recover after such a major event. We've had a bad run of it in 2021 in terms of tricky births, but when you've got a happy mum and a happy calf running around just 12 hours after birth, you can't complain.

Soon after calves are born, they go into the calving pens just outside the parlour for the first couple of weeks. That's where we put any sick or injured animals that need special care and attention or a calving cow we're a bit worried about. It's the place that we travel through most in the day – it kind of feels like the centre of the farm – so we're always checking up on them to make sure they're all right. And that means making sure that they're eating, drinking, growing and bouncing about happily. We bed them up with lots of straw there to keep them warm, but if the outside air temperature drops below 13°C (55°F), we'll fit them with calf jackets, which keep them nice and toasty. It's really important to do this because calves can't regulate their own body temperatures in their first few weeks after birth, and we don't want them to be focusing their energy on staying warm when we need them to be growing and staying healthy.

At around 14 days, when the calves are growing well, we move them out of the calving boxes and into the calf shed. These calves are fed 3 litres of milk twice a day (when they're growing at the fastest rate) until they're ten weeks old, then we start to wean them off milk. Most farms will start to wean them around six weeks, but I like to see the calves really push on and they do this best on milk. A few years ago, we started upping the amount of milk that we give the calves from 2 litres either side of the day to 3 litres, and this has really helped them do even better.

And this work is vital because we want to make sure that the dairy heifers are ready to see the bull for the first time when they're 14–15 months old. If one falls behind (and this applies to the dairy heifers and the beef stock), it's quite hard for them to catch up. That's why I think it's so important to feed them in individual pens up until they're around five weeks old. If a calf is a bit slow and is in a pen of two, three or four, he or she will get bullied out. The other calves will become stronger because they're getting more of the milk and, in turn, the slow one will be getting less, and this can lead to huge issues.

Depending on the time of year we start to turn the dairy heifers out to graze outside at around four or five months old. If we're at the beginning of the summer, when grass is growing and the sun will be on their backs, a four-month-old heifer will do well outside, but you would never start turning them out at that age in September or October because they'd just go backwards. Like everything in farming, the time of year and the weather make a big difference.

At around 15 months old, we separate the beef stock from the dairy heifers. We don't want our beef cattle to see the bull,

so we put them in a completely different field to graze. Ideally in a field that's at least two or three fences away, because, although they literally weigh a ton (and well over that), a randy bull will jump fences if there's a female nearby!

All being well, after the heifers have calved for the first time and start to produce milk, they'll join the Highs group. And as of October 2021, they won't be in the Highs building any more. They'll be in one group in a brand new shiny shed. Living the dream!

6

THE NEW SHED

The new shed is a massive deal for us here and took up a lot of 2021. But building it wasn't the original plan. Yes, we knew we needed to do something about the Lows building, which has served us so well but is completely and utterly knackered. It was built in 1960 as an old army shed and was second-hand when it came to us. My grandad bought it for £1,200, including putting it up. Now, though, it's got more holes than a fancy shower head, it lets in a lot of water and it's only got space for 42 cows to feed, which isn't ideal when bearing in mind we have 64 cows in it. So they can't all feed at once, which is a bit annoying, although it's something I've got used to. There's space for 84 to lie down, though, so it's not all bad. The first idea was to just re-roof the Lows building and build a new feed station. Then we started thinking about knocking the shed down and replacing it with a 9 metre by 27 metre second-hand shed with a new roof on. But that wouldn't have been anywhere near big enough.

Then I was invited by GEA (a tech company who produce farm robots, among other things) to go and check out Shaun

Hartley's new state-of-the-art shed in Clitheroe, and you can't go there without standing back and thinking, 'Wow – that's an impressive operation.' All the cows are in one shed (the dream) and he doesn't have to keep moving stuff about. So it kind of twigged that if there was a way of getting all my cows in one shed, it would make things so much more efficient, so much cleaner and we'd probably see all sorts of knock-on improvements in terms of cow health and milk production. So we hatched a new plan. Build a new shed.

Only, once you've spent ages coming to that decision, you've got a whole shed-load of other questions, like 'How the hell are we going to fund it?' and 'What's the shed even going to look like?' Plus you've got the headache that is applying for planning permission and then paying for it, and wow, I had no idea it was so dear. Fortunately, YouTube had been doing well, we'd sorted out sponsorship with farming companies that worked well with the channel, and the merch sales had been ticking along nicely, so I'd saved up some money that way. Every single Like, subscription and comment has helped me get to this point, so all my viewers are invested in this shed! But you still have to borrow a lot to take on something on the scale that we were imagining, even if the interest rates were really good at that point in time. It's something that doesn't sit right with me – I don't like borrowing too much money if there's any way I can avoid it and I don't spend money on anything unless I need to. That's why my sister Penny, who is now my accountant, calls me a squirrel. I've always been like that, never buying anything

I can't afford – I'd rather work my arse off to try and minimise any debt we have to take on. It's just the way I am and I know that other folks approach things in other ways and they do just fine.

After we got the financials sorted, we got in touch with Wareing, the construction company near us that we've been working with for decades, and started sorting out what kind of shed we'd need and how it could work best for us. So many things to make decisions about, like what cubicles do you go for, are you going to be using a scraper tractor or automated scrapers, what are you going to bed the animals up on, are you going to have slats connecting to the slurry system and where should they go, and what should the pitch of the roof be, among about a thousand others. But making a video about it and putting these questions out to my audience really helped. A problem shared and all that. Also, there have been a lot of times where someone will comment on a video and the answer I've been looking for suddenly reveals itself!

So the work all started in March 2021 with Andrew Wareing, the 70-something boss (and legend) at Wareing getting into his excavator and digging a trial hole in the ground to check what the foundations were going to be sitting on so they could give us a full quote. 'Dig a hole, and it'll tell all,' as Andrew W says. The good news was that under the ground was in better shape than he expected – blue clay rather than running sand, which is what Dad feared, so it would be able to hold concrete foundations. But it did mean you couldn't put in a slurry tank underneath. And that was a bit of a shame because, as every dairy farmer will know, the biggest issue these days is having too much muck at the wrong time of year. But the main thing was that we could build!

And then, a month later, I was moving troughs and feeders, moving the midden (shifting some of it to the local allotments to help their compost out) and taking down the temporary shelter for the Highlands to prepare for Demolition Day. I'll recycle everything I can, save the pennies, save the pounds, the pounds save the hundreds, the hundreds save the thousands, and the thousands are what you spend on sheds! It was a pretty exciting day, because it felt like the beginning of something huge. The next day I had Pete Marquis – the scrap king – on the phone and he'd be coming round in a few days to start demolishing stuff. 'So if you want it, Tom, move it!' Message received, so me and Dad needed to strip out and salvage anything we wanted from the Lows building. And that started with 80+ cow mats at 37kg (82lb) a pop and then going to town with the angle grinder on the hay racks. Mats out, racks out. And I've said it before and I'll say it again: destroying things is a dream job. Cutting out 80 steel cubicles was hard-ass work, but I was all set with my goggles, ear defenders and long TP denim shirt. I was oozing safety right then, people, because, as I may also have said before, danger doesn't take a day off. Goggles didn't look so great after I was done, though – with so much sweat it felt like I was in a fish tank. Lovely! Looking out over the shed after that day, there was definitely no turning back now. And I was cream crackered.

The next day was D-Day and the biggest day on the farm for a long time. I got a bit nervous (nervous excitement, maybe) while I was setting up some time-lapse cameras around the farm so you guys could check out the progress. And then Pete turned up, and him and his boys had a brew before Hazmat-suiting up because the roof sheets that made up the shed had a bit of asbestos going on. Pete and Co absolutely smashed through it, nearly getting through all the roof sheets by the end of the first day and starting to take apart the wooden beams and steel frame and sorting everything into separate piles of good wood, good steel and scrap. All nice and tidy.

I had to leave early that day to go for my and Joanna's wedding tasting, and when I came in to the farm the next morning, it looked like the world had ended. There was nothing there any more out the back of the nursery pens except twisted metal and sky. On day three of the job, Pete was knocking down the remaining wall and picking out the groundworks. Plus we were taking down the old slurry separator and removing the frame. Then Dad and I had to put up a bunch of security fencing that Wareing were dropping over so we could stop the cows from wandering into anywhere that no longer had a wall to contain them. One thing that was pretty cool was that next to and under the separator were a whole bunch of cobbles that looked like part of an old pavement or a shipping floor. Aaron, one of Pete's boys, told me he'd never seen anything like it in ten years of the job. And Pete, by the way, has more skill in his little finger with a 36-tonne digger than anyone I've ever seen. He could practically paint a picture fit for the Queen with that digger. Unbelievable.

Then Pete got to use his brand new £220,000 36-tonne crusher, which smashed up all the waste concrete material using an oscillating jaw into much smaller chunks that we can use as sub-base (an aggregate mix that forms a load-bearing base layer) for the new shed. Love it – smash it up, reuse it and recycle it so we don't have to pay to have the big bits of concrete removed before buying back in the smaller stuff for the new shed foundations. As Pete says, 'It turns rubbish into money. It's a bit like a mobile quarry.' And seriously, what a fantastic bit of kit, and the power it generates to crush the massive bits of concrete up. Wow.

The next job was to start on the groundworks for the new shed. We're very lucky to have nice neighbours who have been pitching in doing favours here and there with dumper trucks on days where we've been struggling a bit in terms of manpower and machine power. I like the way our community here works like that – we all help each other out when needed. Ken, who's done all sorts of big jobs on our farm over the 45 or so years that he's known the Ginger Warrior, was busy digging about 20cm (8in) down and then putting Terram down (a speciality material that allows water to drain through while making sure that stone and soil layers don't mix, which helps keep the foundation solid). On top of that came the aggregate that Pete chopped up for us, then a plastic membrane, another layer of aggregate on top of that and then they started pouring the concrete. The first concrete got poured into the six corners so they could fix the six base plates that the huge steel columns would screw into.

I spent quite a bit of time looking through everything with Chris Wareing and Matt Hastwell, their senior draughtsman, who put together the amazing 3D renderings of the new shed. Because we were building on a 'brownfield' site (an area which used to have a building on it), we had many more issues than we would have had if we built on a 'greenfield' site (an area that hasn't been built on before). We only had a certain amount space to play with and every inch was important, which is why Wareing were so good. I must have changed my ideas and plans five times, but that was no problem. They re-measured with the laser and fed back the new numbers into the computer to make sure it could fit.

You can even access a walkthrough on your phone when you're actually on site to see exactly what everything's going to be, which blew my mind. This kind of tech makes it a lot easier to make decisions like reducing the size of the cubicles from 1.2 metres to 1.1 metres so we can fit another seven cows in the shed comfortably. Matt also told me that I could press the button to cut our last steel beam, so I can say I cut it. I'm also going to put a bolt in so I can say I built it. And then I'll bring the cows in when the time comes, so I've basically done everything.

If the new shed wasn't enough going on, we decided to put up a new second cut silage clamp next to the new first cut clamp. We did this because we normally put our second cut grass into the 'show room' (the indoor shed next to the clamp), but with everything going on we had completely destroyed the concrete in front of it. Tractors couldn't get in or out and there was no way of tipping a 7-metre trailer. We had to get started and only had six weeks to do it!

In fairness to Wareing, they coped with this massive change of plan like absolute pros, and before I knew it they were digging big old holes and pouring concrete again for the huge steel column legs to sit on. But before that, I needed to take out the wooden and wire fences that sat where we were going to need to put the steels in. Only, this idiot did the job wearing shorts when the whole fence was lined with stinging nettles. I redeemed myself a bit by using the Manitou to pull out the posts, though, and that worked a charm. And then, about two weeks after pouring the concrete, the massive steel columns arrived. Twenty minutes later, no joke, two of them, and the strengthener that runs between them, were up. Plus, I got to put a hard hat on and a hi-vis jacket (thanks to Andrew Wareing for that one), so I looked the part even if I wasn't actually doing anything. It was a bit higher than I expected and I worried that Mother would absolutely murder me when she looked out of the kitchen window that morning, but we are planning to plant some tall trees around the perimeter. Plus we're going to stick a roof on top of both clamps with the help of a government grant at some point in the next two, five, ten or twenty years. Definitely not this year or the next, though!

Wisdom from the Ginger Warrior

'The columns are pretty impressive. Yeah, they're big. Big, big, big. However, there's no point thinking about going backwards. This is ideal for the size of trailers these days and it gives the hauliers plenty of room to tip their wagons. And if the silage clamp doesn't work out, we could house a lot of people in here!'

Next, Mick and the lads over the road started on the groundworks for us, levelling everything, then putting the Terram down, then the chopped-up aggregate that Pete ran through his crusher, then a plastic membrane, then more aggregate (this one MOT sub-base, which is much finer), then the mesh sheets to reinforce the concrete and reduce cracking. That'll all make sure that nothing goes down and nothing comes up. Solid as a rock. Then in comes the concrete from the mixer, thick and fast. And fast is something you need to be when you're working with concrete. They poured about 15cm worth and that felt like a lot. Next, Mick and the boys go to town with the rakes and the screed boards to tamp it down because one thing concrete doesn't do for you is level itself.

The next time I videoed the clamp was after my wedding, and all sorts had gone on on the farm. Mick and the lads had installed the walls on the sides of the clamp and me and the Ging had a walk round and were well pleased. We'd angled the floor slightly to ensure that effluent from the clamp runs towards the slurry store (and not towards the fields), so we can link it all up to our existing drains. The new clamp is built for expansion, so we can add another set of panels on the top of the existing walls if we want to. It'll hold as much as we'll need. To sweep the concrete floor, which had a few stones around here and there and little bits of concrete that had dried up and flaked off, we got the Manitou, stuck a bale of straw on the front (we'd actually run out, but thanks to our neighbours for bunging us one) and scraped it along the floor. It's a good makeshift massive broom when you need one. All ready for the second cut to come in.

Next up on the new shed front were the steel columns. They weren't as big as the ones for the new silo clamp (4.5 metres high compared with a monster 7.5 metres tall), but the new shed has a 22.5-degree pitch roof, unlike the clamp (well, for now, anyway). 'New shed' sounds a bit boring now, come to think of it. Maybe I need to come up with something better. The cow house, the cow hotel, the moo-tel perhaps?

Not even sorry for that one. Andrew Wareing was telling me that they'd added a handrail around the perimeter of the roof and part of the framework for that they try and get into place before the columns are in position. So when they're ready to get the roof on, there's a safety rail to stop any of the guys from sliding off.

That moment when the first steel column went up was a big one for me. I never thought this kind of thing would be happening on our little dairy farm, but it's happening, people! By the end of the day, three columns were up, plus the support beams and the diagonal reinforcement bar at the end. And the next morning at 8.30, the Wareing guys had already put five columns up. It was a real case of blink and you'll miss it, but I had the time-lapse cameras set up by then, so no bother. Got myself a nice view of everything from the slurry tower, too. We had all the equipment here that day as well, the Bobcat (which Andrew W swears by because of its boom-positioning system), two cherry pickers and two cranes to shift the four 15-metre rafters. 'We've got more equipment here than we have in our own yard,' the big man told me. And wow, seeing those first two rafters go up was an amazing feeling, because it's the first time you can see the shape of it start to come together.

This scene had been four years in the making, dreaming and talking about this moment and wondering if we could ever make it happen. But if there's one thing that working as a dairy farmer teaches you, it's the patience to see your time and effort come together to create something special.

One thing I didn't know (well, there's more than one thing I learned that day, if I'm honest) is that you have to keep the rafters in position with the cranes, even though they've been bolted together fine, because there's no longitudinal stability in it at that point. It's only when you put the second rafter frame up and add the wind bracing that it gives it a strong, rigid core. 'Once the second frame and its bracings are in, it's bulletproof. But if you let go of the rafters now with the two cranes, it could wander,' as Andrew W tells me.

Once the rafters are in place, the Wareing guys start fitting safety netting to them to prevent anyone working on the roof, and especially fitting the roof panels, from dropping through it. Chris Wareing joked with me that the netting should be able to support the weight of a Mini. Or perhaps Carl, the biggest of the Wareing guys, who's at least 6ft 6in and wouldn't look out of place playing No. 8 for the England rugby team.

I know we get a bad rep as farmers for not being health and safety conscious. There's a kind of 'It'll be all right' approach that you hear a lot in farming. I'm definitely guilty of it, and then there's the feeling that you're protected because you're young, strong, quick and in (fairly) good shape. But sometimes, I'll go to an event and someone will come along and share something that really makes people sit up and take notice. It probably doesn't come as a massive surprise to most of you that farming has the worst rate of fatal injuries across all of the industry sectors. But what did surprise me is that farming has the worst fatality rate by such a long way, like 20 times higher than the average fatality rate in industry in general. And although the stats are better than they were in the 1980s and 1990s, it's pretty much levelled off from 2010 onwards. The period from 1 April 2019 to 31 March 2020 was one of the best for a long time, but that still means that 23 people working in Ag in the UK lost their lives. And the following year, to March 2021, it went up to 41 people – just shy of a 100 per cent rise. And over half the victims were over 60 as well.

It's easy to read stats and not be that bothered by them, thinking that it just won't happen on our farm. I get it. But when you listen to people who sound and seem like yourself doing exactly what you get up to on a farm, telling you about an accident or a tragedy, it sinks in. In 2021, one farmer was killed after a tractor tyre he was inflating exploded, causing massive head injuries. Yeah, a freak accident for sure. But he was only 23.

But it's not just machinery, moving vehicles and accidents involving cows and bulls. It's also falling from heights. A farmer in Hampshire was killed after falling from a shed roof while he was removing roof sheets. There wasn't a safety net. Another farmer, David Anker, in Bedfordshire, was paralysed recently after falling from a grain-store roof, but he survived thanks to the air ambulance arriving quickly. He told a webinar set up by NFU East Anglia that, 'We all think we are indestructible – I did. I have worked at height on many occasions over the past 40 years.' He wasn't insured, so not only has he lost his source of income, he's also had to move out of his farmhouse because it's not suitable for wheelchairs. So maybe the 'It'll be all right' approach will slowly change to 'It'll be all right . . . until it's not, so do something about it.' Maybe we should be thinking about it in terms of marginal gains. Spend a bit more time and effort here and there, sticking on goggles or wearing the safety hat, to lead to a big overall improvement. I know it's different because it's more difficult to see the fruits of your labours when you're working hard to make sure something *doesn't* happen. But David Anker has had to fork out £250,000 to cover the change to his life. And he's one of the luckier ones.

Benny, one of the Wareing legends working on the new shed, told us how he once fell through a roof panel he'd been putting up. It had a crack in it that no one had seen. Only, Benny had a safety net fitted under the roof, which saved his life. Yeah, it hardly ever happens – Benny's been working on roofs for decades and has only had one thing like that happen. But if you're given a straight choice between spending a few hours putting up a safety net and falling into it when a roof panel breaks, or not putting up a net, saving an hour and taking a 9-metre drop back to Earth, I know which one I'd go for. And I know the one Benny would go for, too.

If you've seen my videos, you know that I don't cut out bits where I've ballsed something up – I want to show people what happens here and what we do to fix or sort something that goes wrong. I do think it's important to make some mistakes so you learn from them, but sometimes you don't need to experience the mistake to learn from it. Sometimes, and this is mainly for the young folks in Ag, I hope you can learn from my cock-ups! As the channel has got more successful than I ever imagined, though, and I realise that I'm reaching more people, I really want to set a good example. And that's why you've probably heard me or the Ginger Guy mentioning that 'danger doesn't take a day off'. I like to think we're getting more conscious of health and safety on the farm and raising awareness for some of the organisations that do some amazing work, like Yellow Wellies.

Yellow Wellies (or The Farm Safety Foundation as they're known officially) was set up in 2014 as a charity to help the next generation of farmers with health and safety. Their key goal is to bring down the number of avoidable deaths on farms to zero, and that's an aim that everyone in agriculture shares. And to try and achieve this, they post farm-safety messages, hold farm-safety training educational programmes and launch national campaigns like Farm Safety Week and Mind Your Head, which focuses on mental health in farming. Mental health in farming is a big issue that has gone overlooked for a long time, partly because people find it difficult to talk about it. But we've got to start talking about it, because 133 people in agriculture and associated agricultural trades took their own lives in 2019–20. That's nearly six times the number of people who lost their lives in accidents on farms. So the biggest danger some of us face in farming is being able to cope with what we do. Farming is not for everyone. You spend the vast majority of your working day on your own, often in a remote location. And since then, we've had a pandemic, where us farmers have been working our arses off even more than usual and spending more time alone than we would ordinarily do.

I'm an upbeat guy, I love what I do, I care for my animals and I've got an amazing family and team here on the farm. Not only that, but I receive loads of kind comments from people that really cheer me up if I'm having a rough day. But even with that support network, I have some low moments here. Saying goodbye to Neptune and Toby, for example, or finding that a calf hasn't made it through the night, have been tough times. I can't imagine what that would be like if I was already struggling.

And back in December 2017, I *was* struggling, and it's something only a few friends and family know about. I didn't know how to talk about it on a video back then, but I want to tell you about it here in case it helps someone. I was helping out in the farm shop a lot at that time, on top of what I was usually doing on the farm, and we got completely overwhelmed by orders from customers. The shop wasn't equipped to deal with them because it was the first Christmas we were open and we'd taken hundreds of orders (we now have a better system, thankfully). I couldn't cope with the stress and I didn't know what to do or who to ask for help. I remember going to bed at 2am one night in the farmhouse and walking over to work at 5.30. Then someone at the shop said, 'Are you all right, Tom, you don't look very well?' and I just started crying. I walked out the back of the shop, ignored everyone in my path, went over to the farmhouse and headed upstairs. I found my sister Amy, who helped calm me down. And it wasn't the first time that I'd turned to my elder sister when I had a problem I needed help with, especially when I was younger. She's honest, dependable, kind and knows what to do in a crisis.

It was such a weird feeling, though. I can't remember ever having something like that happen before and I didn't really know what was going on. I felt like I'd hit a wall and I couldn't even go into the farm shop for about a month after that. It took a lot for me to walk through that door again. I later realised while talking on a live video with someone that I'd probably had a panic attack. I couldn't cope with the amount of stress, I was too tired and I just imploded. I feel like I've learned a lot from that scary time, though, and how to recognise the signs to look out for, telling me that I need to take a break.

If you're struggling and don't know where to turn, there is an organisation you can call. It's called Farming Help (03000 111 999) and they offer impartial, confidential advice to farmers who do need help. In Scotland, contact RSABI on their helpline 0300 111 4166.

Next to arrive for the new shed are the cement-fibre roof panels and the roof lights, both of which are made by Eternit, a British company who can trace back a long partnership with Wareing. Their roof sheets are British made, they should last for 50 years and they're fully recyclable. You might remember their name because Stuart from Eternit came down to the farm while the Lows building was still standing, armed with an arsenal of smoke bombs. Stuart is a great guy and, like me, he loves numbers. And he's one of those people who have helped make this shed what it is.

What Stuart does is conduct a series of tests to monitor a building's temperature, windspeed, humidity, light and noise. And when he's done crunching the numbers, he'll make recommendations for how to optimise that building, and a lot of that will be about improving airflow. Good airflow helps make cows happy and healthy. So I took it on board and went about trying to make the best improvements we could with the budget we had.

The first thing I learned about our Lows building is that the humidity was 44 per cent outside, but 59 per cent inside the shed, because the concrete's damp and there's more moisture in the air. If we had cows in the shed, Stuart tells me the humidity would be in the nineties. Heat stress can be a big problem because it means that the cows are using up energy regulating their body temperature rather than directing the energy to producing milk. Milking cows generate up to 40 per cent more heat than dry ones and they've got to get rid of that heat if they're going to stay productive. The way you do that is by getting as much fresh air as possible coming in over the top of the cows. Fortunately, in our old Lows building, it's so full of holes (both intentionally made and not) that we've actually improved the humidity over the years! And the light levels are great, too! But, as Stuart tells me, while the ventilation stats might have got better, it hasn't exactly helped with cow comfort. Hmmm, he might have a point there.

As great as it is hearing about statistics and cows, let's let off some smoke grenades! Although it wasn't such great news for the Lows building. It turns out the air recirculates in the middle of the building and hardly any of it disperses upwards, so if any animal's ill with pneumonia, for example, there's a strong chance she's going to spread it to other cows all around her. Also, you realise that the higher cows up in the hierarchy choose the best places to lie and feed in a shed, so the more subordinate cows end up in the least desirable places with the least light and ventilation, so they naturally don't perform as well as the others. That's one of the reasons I wanted to turn the new shed into a place where every single space for the cows is near enough the same.

One statistic that Stuart quoted me that absolutely blew my mind was that ventilation can impact milk yield by up to 10 per cent. Seeing as our cows graze outside for six months of the year, this is more like 5 per cent, but with 110 cows, who produce an average of 25 litres each a day (across the Highs and Lows), a 5 per cent loss equals 1.25 litres (or 2 pints) per cow. So that's 130-odd litres a day. That works out as around £32 a day loss, which is nearly £1,000 a month or £12,000 a year. Over a building's lifespan of, say, 50 years, that would add up to a loss of £600,000. Wow. Thanks, Stuart! On that note, it was time for a brew.

Another thing I had no idea about was how heat stress can

be a problem even in March and October, let alone summer. In the space of just 20 minutes, the temperature of the roof lights in the Highs shed went up from 13°C to 18°C (that's 55°F to 65°F). If it reaches 20°C (68°F), bearing in mind the humidity in the shed when all the cows are in it, the cows will start to suffer the effects of heat stress on their productivity. On top of that, it took over seven and a half minutes for the smoke bomb to completely disperse, compared with two minutes fifteen seconds in the Lows shed. So, quite amazingly, after we crunched Stuart's numbers, it turns out the Highs shed is in worse shape than the Lows shed, which we're knocking down. D'oh! But, to make me feel better, he told me that the Highs shed is no different to 90 per cent of the old farms he goes to. The new shed, on the other hand, will be like 90 per cent of the new farms that he visits. But that's only if I take his advice!

In the end, I did implement a lot of Stuart's advice. We've been using Eternit for the past 50 years, he's been doing this for a long time, knows his stuff and looks round new setups all the time. We went with his suggestion to make the pitch of the roof 22.5 degrees to maximise airflow and cow comfort. We also installed a covered open ridge in the apex of the roof so that stale air can escape but rainwater doesn't enter the building, so my cows are nice and dry. It's basically a 200mm gap between the two sets of roof sheets with a 400mm Perspex cover so that the rain hits the cover and runs down it and onto the roof sheets. The Perspex cover is even angled to account for the fact that the rain in winter batters us from the east. Super-clever stuff. And the third thing was putting twice as many roof lights on the west side of the building, which doesn't get as much light, especially in the winter, so you're letting as much light in as you can without allowing too much heat in, and so you avoid the cows suffering from heat stress.

Talking about heat stress, the Wareing guys were putting up the roof in 30°C+ (86°F+) heat while Jo and I were on mini-honeymoon in the Lake District, enjoying ourselves with a cider. For those of you not from the UK, 30°C is absolutely mental here and happens once in a blue moon. Working 12 metres up without any shade isn't ideal, so you have to have a drinks break every half hour or so just to stay alive. Even so, they'd still put up most of the roof in those few days, despite the steep pitch of the roof that was a bit of a nightmare to walk up. In order to have a proper look at how the roof was looking and what it was like working up there, I faced my fear of heights and went up on the cherry picker. Thanks, Benny!

The first thing I can tell you for free is it's not nice treading on roof sheets, even if you're not scared of heights. And the next thing is that, wow, it's slippy scrambling up roof sheets. Quick shout out to the birds who have already made themselves at home and crapped on my new roof. So I can confirm: it's hard work up here and I wasn't even working. And straight from the big man, Carl: 'It's horrible, yeah!' It was amazing to see the covered open ridge come together, though. It'll be interesting to see what it's like when it starts to rain, but with the most amount of respect to Benny, Carl and Henry on the roof, I'm not going to be up here then. Although having said that, the roof's a great place to call the cows in for milking! And yes, I can tell the numbers of the cows that were coming towards the gate from a good 15 metres up. Does that make me sad?

Lighting for cows is really important and I've learned so much about it during this build. To be healthy and produce good milk, a cow needs to be in a light, bright space, ideally with a light intensity of 180–200 lux. Even the colour of light is important, so we're trying to re-create the effect of May/June daylight all year round. We worked out that we needed 12 lights, and found out how far apart they should be. Currently, the worst spot in the shed measures 139 lux, and while it might not hit the 180 I would have liked, it's a hell of a lot brighter than we've ever had before! We made sure that all the lights are on dimmers, which I can control on an app on my phone. Between 11pm and 5am, all the lights dim down to 40 lux (a bit like moonlight), so the cows can rest. The reason I chose 5am as the time to switch on the lights is that we start milking at six and this gives the cows an hour to fully wake up and have a drink or a bit of breakfast before we get going.

On the subject of food and drink, we've gone for quick-cleaning water troughs. These have a latch that empties the water out in around ten seconds and refills it in eighty depending on water pressure. It's all about making life easy for cows and myself. We added rubber flooring in front of each water trough to make it comfortable for them, because did you know that cows spend 14 per cent of their lives drinking?! Neither did I before I started the project. We also installed a 43-cm wide and 2.5-cm thick area of rubber in front of the feed rail on the floor of the passageway where the cows stand, to take the pressure off their front feet while they're feeding and make them comfortable. The feeding passageway is 10 cm higher than the cows' passageway, so they don't have to reach as far to get their feed, too. This all means the cows are more likely to stay at the feed rail for longer and so hopefully we'll have fewer sole ulcers or abscesses on their front feet. I told you, it's all about making the cows as comfy as we can while they are in for the six months of winter.

The floor was smoothed and levelled with a power-floater by Marc from Ascroft. It now has a glass finish and makes the difference between eating your meal off a lovely smooth bone-china plate rather than a lumpy concrete floor. I know which one I'd choose! Marc even worked until late on a Friday night, missing a festival in Birmingham to make sure the job was done perfectly, which is much appreciated! This was a theme to our new build. Everyone worked so hard and put everything they had in to it.

Choosing cubicles and mattresses was a really hard decision. I kept asking myself: do we go for what we have always gone for – steel cubicles that we've had no issues with before – or choose the new, more flexible plastic/rubber ones which we don't know if they'll stand the test of time the same way? So I did a lot of research and bought the Kingshay dairy consultants' report on nine different mattresses to try and work out which one would fit my system the best. In the end, I went for the Easyfix cubicles and mattresses. They weren't the cheapest, but the mattresses are extra comfy with foam underneath, and the cubicles are made from plastic with rubber fittings and are super flexible. You can see the cows leaning on them and not being restricted at all. Large cows or small cows fit really well and I'm hoping it makes them super chilled.

For the feed rail, we also went for one from Easyfix. I did wonder about installing lock-in yokes (so you can lock the cows in if you need to attend to anything health-wise on them), but I spoke to a farmer who had both lock-in yokes and a feed rail section, and he said the cows chose the feed rail over the lock-in yokes every time! He said they just felt more relaxed and didn't feel there could be a chance to get caught in them. Lock-in yokes are great to get work done with the cows safely, but I have our calving building with ten AI stalls which kind of serves a similar purpose, so I'm hoping I won't miss them too much. And finally, we went for two electric (I know – *electric*, how exciting) cow brushes. That's one for every 60 cows to make sure the girls are super clean and can have a nice rub whatever the time of day.

After the roof was on the shed, we started on the groundworks for the slurry channels. Instead of having slats miles away from the cubicles, which is our current setup, we decided on a central channel in the middle of the new shed, covered by slats, so we could scrape the muck into there. And this neatly joins up with the existing system, too. We also put in slats at the eastern edge of the building, which will link up with the current channels. We decided to dig a third slurry trench at the western edge of the building, too, so if we want to put in robots or a new parlour in the future it will all be set up for it. This all means that now it takes me six passes with the scraper tractor to clean 60 cows out in the new shed, where in the old one it was taking 20 passes to clean 48 cows. It makes our lives easier, saves loads of time and keeps the cows cleaner. And that's a massive win-win in my eyes.

While they were digging the middle trench, the Ascroft lads found a drain that had a crack in which solved the mystery of why our car park was flooding. So they fixed that for us too. Unfortunately, though, we did then hit a major snag. We couldn't buy in slurry channels because there was a 15-week wait for them and we only had eight weeks to get the cows in. So we had to think on our feet and come up with something else. We decided on pouring a concrete base in for each of the three trenches, reinforcing the concrete with mesh and lining the sides in block work. They aren't going to be the deepest channels in the world, but they're not really designed to hold much slurry – they're designed so slurry passes through them on the way to the lagoon. It was a real pain in the arse waiting for the concrete to set, though, because so much moisture was coming up from the ground.

The next morning, more and more ground water had come up into the trenches, so the Ginger Warrior and Andrew

Wareing, with a combined age of 136 years, got to work with the brooms. Then I fetched the Manitou with the pallet forks to move the sand and cement, which had arrived that morning, into position for the blockmen. And then they set about fixing three layers of blocks on each side of each of the three trenches. And they absolutely smashed it.

Next job was to clear out the slurry lagoon. Or the 'bowels of the earth', as Andrew W put it. Not my favourite job, if I'm honest. It meant borrowing a Bobcat from Pete Marquis and getting Andrew W to lower it with a big crane into the lagoon along with a big skip. It'd been left with a horrible crust for so long that we figured now was the time to sort it because it was stopping the lagoon from holding as much slurry as we need it to. And what did I say us dairy farmers struggle with? Storage! Fortunately, I was still a bit hungover from a wedding the night before, so my nose wasn't working properly. After I'd cleared about half the slurry, I was in proper need of a bacon butty. And a little bit of a hand wash. After that fuel, I smashed the rest of it. And it felt great doing something that we'd been meaning to sort for ages. Much like the whole project, come to think of it!

7

THE FUTURE OF THE FARM!

We're a small dairy farm and so there's a limit to what we can do with the land, parlour setup, size of the sheds and feed space. That will change a bit with the new shed, but sometimes, like we did in October 2020, we decide to sell some cows. The herd had grown from 118 (including dry cows) in 2019 to 141 in 2020, plus we had maybe a dozen heifers that were bagging up and due to calve really soon. It's great that our cows are getting in calf so well, but at this moment in time we don't need the extra milk. Anything over and above what we sell on our milk rounds we sell to spot, and by that I mean the spot market where it can be bought by other businesses that need it. The price that you can get for your milk depends on the state of the market, though. In spring, for example, there's a lot of milk about because a lot of cows calve around then and they're turned out onto spring grass, so you don't get a lot of money for your milk. And in October 2020, we'd just gone into another lockdown, so cafes, restaurants, hotels and B&Bs were all shutting their doors and the price of milk on the spot market dipped really low. Meanwhile, though, the price you could get for selling heifers was a little bit higher than it normally was. It was a tough decision, but in the end we called up the dealer.

Before the dealer turns up, I just give the heifers a check to make sure they're clean and eating and drinking nicely. Then we move them to the collection yard in front of the parlour for the dealer to take a look at them. In the end, we sold all four of them, three for £1,800 and one that had recently calved for £1,600, so that's £7k in the bank, and that sort of money pays a feed bill for a whole month. It's not something I really like to do, though – I'm not keen on selling cows and much prefer to keep them here their whole lives, looking after them and getting the best out of them we can, but sometimes it makes sense. It's hard to think with your head rather than your heart when you've invested a lot of time and effort into them, but this is the deal with helping to run a business. I hope the heifers go on to do well, stay healthy and happy and make lots of milk at the next farm.

But in April 2021, we decided to take on a bit more land: an L-shaped sloped field with a pond at the top, a long straight field with a few drainage issues at its lower end that are being sorted by the landowner and a 28-acre field (which is pretty huge for us) that has gone a bit sour. To be precise, we're taking on about 30 more acres, because two fields that we're renting at the moment we're giving back to the owner. The third field has got quite a few issues: it was very wet in the winter so it's been left with bare patches, there are molehills springing up all over the place and it hasn't had any feeding with fertiliser or muck for some years. All land needs feeding.

We had the same sort of problems with some of the land we took on four years ago, but we've turned those fields around nicely and made them productive, and we're planning to do the same with the new land. It just needs a good bit of TLC and it'll be all right. On the first two fields, we'll use the sward lifter (see page 64) once the owner has fixed the drainage issues. On the third, big, field, we'll get some fertiliser down straight away, give it a good harrowing with the chain harrows to get the dead grass out and see how it's doing after that. Then we might use the slitter to get some air into the roots, because they'll need a bit of work after being sat under water for long stretches. After that, we'll roll it, but not much – we don't want to undo the slitting work by filling up the holes up. Then we'll reseed it but only after the field's dry. Also, we need to find out where all the drains are, something that the Ginger Warrior will take great pleasure in!

The third field hasn't half got a good view: Lytham Hall, an 18th-century Georgian country house that looks like something out of *Pride and Prejudice*, is just across the path, so the drone shots when we get round to cutting this field are going to be amazing! We're quite proud of Lytham Hall up here. It's the only Grade I listed building in Fylde and is owned by the Lytham Town Trust and managed by the Heritage Trust for the North West. It was owned by the Clifton family since 1606, but the last owner, Henry de Vere

Clifton, sold off much of the estate in the early 1960s. He was quite a character by all accounts, a racehorse owner, amateur jockey, actor, film producer and poet, but he squandered all his money in casinos and ended up living out his days in a rundown hotel in Brighton. In 1963 the estate was bought by the Guardian Royal Exchange Insurance Company, who used the hall for offices, but in 2001 the Lytham Town Trust bought it back for the local community with help from a donation from BAE Systems. Lytham Hall is now staffed by volunteers – all credit to them – and it's a cracking place to visit if you're in the area.

Thankfully, we get on really well with the landowner – we help him out when he needs it and he returns the favour. It was his boys who helped pour the concrete on the new clamp. And he knows that we'll look after the land and improve it, so everyone's a winner, including the visitors to Lytham Hall, who will see a lovely lush field hopefully in a year or so.

We didn't hang about, though. Dad was even happy for me to get on with the till sowing, something he usually does himself, in the new third field the morning after we shot the video about the extra land we'd taken on. Which meant that I got to do one of my favourite things: holding two bags of fertiliser above the till sower with the Manitou and cutting into the bottom of the bags. Then watch the sower fill up in seconds. So satisfying! Very weird, I know...

I put five bags of till on the field in the end. Two bags usually do about 12 acres, but a little extra won't hurt this field. I didn't try and get the fertiliser too close to the edges because there were so many wet patches. In fact, it had got so wet that bulrushes were growing in the field next to Liggard Brook, the drain that runs into the Ribble estuary. You always know a field is super wet if you've got rushes finding a home there. Then I attached the chain harrows to the Case Vestrum. It was the first time I'd used them in a few years and I was pretty excited about cracking on, but then I got a call from Heids, who needed a hand catching a couple of newborn lambs so we could tag them up and do their tails. It was a busy old time that day, milking cows, putting till on, washing the till sower, spotting a new Highland calf on the farm (!) and then helping Heids catch what turned out to be the fastest lambs I've ever seen. About time to grab a wrap and a coffee and get back in the Case to do some harrowing. Living the dream for the next few hours, people!

Meanwhile, the Ginger Warrior was aboard a digger with one of the landowner's boys. The hole that he reckoned was a drain when we first inspected the field on the Case did turn out to be one. So he was well happy. 'It's a great big drain, it's amazing' were his words. I love how excited Dad gets about drains. He's absolutely mad for them, it's like he's struck gold or oil or something. But then I found a manhole while I was working on the field with the chain harrows and I realised that I get exactly as excited by drains as the Ginger Warrior, thinking about the maze of pipes under the field. It's like you've discovered some sort of long-lost secret knowledge, and armed with that you might be able to repair them and get the field draining again properly. I'm a Pemberton, after all – I was always gonna be a sucker for a drain. So I gave Dad a ring and they went over to the manhole with the digger to check out what was underneath. Next he'll get them jetted and cleaned out and we might be able to bring this field back to life.

I could have kept going with the chain harrow for a lot longer, but it was 2.30 and I had to get back for milking at 3 and hopefully get on with the harrowing after that. That is one of the chief pains in the arse of being a dairy farmer on a busy farm. You have to keep stopping and starting on jobs, but on the flip side, I love what I do, so I'll just keep going on this into the evening.

The next day, I attached the slitter – basically a rotating drum with loads of blades on it, which aerate the ground. Have you ever seen the groundsmen and women at half time stabbing the pitch at a football game? Imagine that, but on an industrial scale.

I gave the slitter a good dose of grease before we got started. This time I was using the Hürlimann and it did make me miss the comfy Case a bit. Although I'm glad to hand it over to Dad to spare his knees for a while. In the Case, there's not so much stopping and starting, not so much back and forth on the clutch all day. It's just a much cleverer machine. Oh, and the speedometer works in the Case, which is a plus. I did take the opportunity to get the drone up with Lytham Hall in the foreground and the Ribble estuary in the background. Magic. Next, Dad got hold of an overseeder from Hoyles, which plants seeds down into the ground. This is a great machine because it means you don't need to plough, cultivate or turn the field – the seed goes straight into the sward and gives the field a new lease of life. It's a great way of adding quality back into the land.

After that, we rolled it. On the other two new fields, all we needed to do was roll them, because they were in much better shape than the third one. And that was it. We'd given the new fields the best chance to grow a cracking crop of grass.

> **Wisdom from the Ginger Warrior**
> 'Ten pence worth of grease will save you having to replace a £100 bearing. Make do and mend!'

Other ways we're thinking about expanding the farm involve bringing in some new animals. We've got Highlands, Jacob sheep, pygmy goats and a Shetland pony, so it's already well on its way to becoming a zoo. I should mention the two ponies we've got here, too. I tend to overlook them, because, well, they scare me and they make a right mess of the fields. Why do they terrify me? It's how quickly they can kick out. I'm a cow guy and cows are chilled almost all of the time, but horses can be so fast and flighty. So I give them a massive berth if I'm walking around their back ends – I've seen the viral video of the guy getting kicked by a horse and I've learned my lesson!

The ponies belong to my sister Penny, who loves them and looks after them. First up is Samuel, our resident Shetland pony. He's black and white (or piebald if we're being technical) and measures 8 hands. A hand is a unit of measurement equivalent to 10cm (4in) and based on the width of a human hand. Horses and ponies are measured to the height of their 'withers', the ridge between their shoulder blades, which is the highest point on their body. I know how to use Google!

I know Shetland ponies look a bit like toy ponies, and they are the smallest breed of pony in the UK, but they're much stronger than they look, have a thick coat and have been put to work doing all sorts in the past, from ploughing to hauling coal out of mines. They've been about for 4,000 years coping with the winters in the Shetland Isles, so they're 'ard. But they're also cute with fluffy manes and kids love 'em. Even if I don't very much...

Our second one is Barney, a grey Connemara pony, the largest of the pony breeds. He's nearly double the height of Samuel at 15.1 hands, so we have got a bit of a 'Little and Large' show going on. He came over from Ireland when he was five, about eight months after Samuel arrived on the farm. They live together in a stable that measures 12 metres by 3.5 metres and it's on sleds so it can move if we need it to. Samuel and Barney are both 16 years old (born within a week of each other, weirdly) and they get on like two peas in a pod, so much so that Samuel gets really sad if Penny's out riding Barney.

Penny comes down before work each day, checks on them, shifts the poos and gives them a bit of attention. Neither of the ponies wears shoes because the new hoof that they grow gets worn down naturally when they're moving about the farm. If they were out and about on roads, Penny would probably need to fit them with shoes to protect their feet. The farrier comes to the farm every eight weeks to check their feet. They get spring and summer baths. Every eight to ten weeks, we come in with the Manitou and pull out the straw. We don't stick it in the midden yet, though – it's still good for the cows!

Back in 2019, after I did the first video about the ponies, I promised that if I got to 200,000 subscribers on YouTube, I'd face my fears and ride a horse. When I said that, I didn't imagine I'd actually get to 200,000, so it felt like a safe bet. A bet that made me look brave without having to do anything about it. Perfect! What an idiot. But, ever a man of my word, in July 2020, when I reached that amazing milestone (probably thanks largely to people who wanted to see me crap myself riding a horse), I agreed to ride Barney. Barney, who whenever he gets let out onto the field jumps around like a bucking bronco. That day, I felt about 60 per cent sure that my number was up. Thankfully, Penny put me at ease straight away with three words of comfort: 'You could die.' Followed by: 'I don't know if your bottom will fit on that seat.' Thanks, Pen. So, full disclosure, I had ridden a horse once before, when I was five, and I cried the whole time. But this time, I tamed the wild stallion. And it wasn't as bad as I thought and Barney, Penny and Des smashed it with the lesson. So will I be getting back on a horse soon? Will I f***!

That month was a pretty amazing one, though, because the BBC got in touch with a few different ideas for shows they wanted me to be involved in. Completely mental. I still find it amazing whenever someone waves at me when they're driving down Ballam Road, so this absolutely *blew* my mind. Those conversations ended up in the show *The Fast and the Farmer(ish)* (get it?), which I'm presenting. That still doesn't feel real saying it. I flew to Ireland in September 2020 and we filmed the pilot.

The idea is there are teams from England, Scotland, Wales and Northern Ireland who compete in all sorts of wacky events and challenges driving their own souped-up tractors. It was a lot of fun to film and we had such a laugh. And, amazingly, the pilot was really well received, so the series went ahead. The announcement happened in April 2021, in the *Daily Mail*, the *Daily Express*, the *Daily Mirror*, the *Sun*, everywhere! That was probably my biggest pinch-yourself moment in this funny old YouTube rollercoaster.

I went over to Ireland in July 2021 to film for ten days, then headed back for a week in September (yup, while the new shed was going up). I did get a bit apprehensive in front of 40 people on set with the pressure on me to try to gel everything together, but I gave it the beans, so fingers crossed everyone likes it. I was really nervous right before filming started, but like the first proper speech I did at Dairy-Tech in 2018, I really enjoyed it when I was up there talking, and I came away thinking, 'I'd like to do more of this!' Jo liked the first runs of the show a lot, but I found it hard to watch myself, the same way that I found it difficult when I watched my first few YouTube videos back. I think that's just because I feel like I've no idea what I'm doing, even if other people watching it think otherwise.

Going forward, how do I see my future on the farm? Well, my parents are 64 years young and are looking to slow down, so I'm going to take more of a leading role soon. I want to improve the milking parlour and like the idea of adding a viewing area over it so people can see the cows being milked at certain times. With a brew in hand from the café next door. Well, that's the dream! I want to give more to the end consumer, like we do now, but offer them even more of an experience of farm life. And maybe arrange more school visits as well. With the platform I have through social media I'd love to keep spreading all the good that farmers do around the UK. And there's no better way of doing that than getting people to come to the farm and see the place for themselves.

As for other ventures, I'd like to keep saying yes to things. It sounds really daft, but it's so easy to be comfortable doing what you do. I know because I was that guy. But I feel like I've grown in the four years I've been making my videos and now, weirdly, some of the things that I used to be the most nervous about are the most enjoyable. Like standing in front of a bunch of cameras while a whole TV crew and contestants are waiting for you to do something. And if more opportunities come my way, I'll take them with both hands! If not, then I'll be happy making my YouTube videos, improving the farm and topping up my coffee each morning with the freshest, creamiest milk around before I start the day with my girls.

Q & A WITH TOM PEMBERTON

Hello there, dear readers! I hope this message finds you well. As you already know (because you've read the book, right? Not just skipped to the back . . .), I am Tom Pemberton, farmer, content creator and author of *Make Hay While the Sun Shines*. It's a little while since I wrote the book, and I wanted to provide you all with an update on life on the farm. I've been keeping busy with various projects and learning experiences, and I'm excited to share some of them with you today. So without further ado, here are a few questions that I've put together to give you an idea of what's been happening since the book was published. Thank you for your continued support, and I hope you enjoy reading these updates as much as I've enjoyed writing them.

Q The response to the book has been amazing, making it into the *Sunday Times* bestseller list. What did it mean to you to see so many people responding so positively to the book?

A Crazy mental . . . If you'd told the 14–15-year-old Tom that he would have had, one, a book released by a huge publisher and then, secondly, got a *Sunday Times* bestseller, he would have laughed at you – and so would the rest of the class he was with.

Q How would you say life on the farm has changed in the last year?

A Massively in one way and all the same the next. We still milk the cows twice a day, we still feed them, muck them out, take care of them. But this past year we've had a full winter in the new shed, which has been bliss: it's cleaned the farm up and made the little things a hell of a lot easier. We are just getting ready for one of the biggest chapters of my career – a brand new milking parlour. Things are about to get busy again.

Q You always discuss very openly the challenges that come with working on the farm. What would you say are the biggest challenges you faced in the last year and how did you work through them?

A Time management 100 per cent . . . One of my biggest flaws is that I want to do everything but struggle to juggle it all. Things are getting busier and busier both on and off the farm, and the off-the-farm stuff needs my time. The bit I love most is the time on the farm, so I struggle to give it up. But the things that happen off the farm normally bring in more than the farm could ever do . . . It's something I'm still working on.

Q What are your goals and plans for the farm in the future? Where do you see it going?

A I think a huge plan is to get the new parlour sorted . . . This would save an hour to an hour and a half in the morning and hopefully an hour in the evening. That would give me more time to do all the things I want to do.

I would love to have the farm more open to the general public. After six years we have just put a new raw milkshake vending machine in and the feedback has been incredible. The family cannot believe it. It's increased the sales by four to five times. We have the goats on offer in the old dog kennel (it's a lot bigger than it sounds) and while people are getting their shakes they come to look at the goats. This makes me feel like the viewing area I want to create has the potential to be really successful. Hopefully . . . That's with everything crossed.

Q Away from the farm, what are the personal goals that you have been working on over the past year, or any that you have for the future?

A I have signed up for a 10k run in Manchester and also put my name down for the Great North half-marathon. Fingers crossed I get it.

Q You now have over 500,000 subscribers on YouTube. How do you stay motivated to keep making videos and coming up with new ideas, especially with the long working hours on the farm?

A It's been a incredible ride and to hit 500k was amazing. I think I keep motivated because I had worked on the farm for eight or nine years before social media and the last three years have been a whirlwind. We have been able to do things on the farm that I could never have imagined . . . Pushed it 20–30 years forwards. It's something I'm really passionate about, enjoy and just want to get better every year if I can.

Q You have been very open, on social media and in the book, when discussing your own mental-health struggles and the stress that the job can have on you. Particularly with the challenges many people are facing now, what are some ways you have found to look after yourself and your own mental wellbeing/health?

A We make sure we have regular time off – we work the 12 on/2 off system. That means we have two days off roughly every two weeks. What works for me as well is trying to do some kind of exercise, be it runs or jumping on a bike. I don't know about you, but when I'm running and trying to beat a time or even trying to get to the next lamp post, my brain is not thinking about the farm – I'm just trying to get to the end. This really helps me chill out. The other big one is the family. I'm very, very lucky to have my family around me. I see them regularly. If I need some advice I can ring the wife, sisters, parents or even best mates. Even if I haven't spoken to them for a while, I know I can ring them whenever and they feel the same about me. We often text or ring if it's been over three or four months and just put the world to rights.

Q If you had to give one 'Tom's Top Tip' with everything you have learned over the past year, what would it be?

A A diamond is formed under a major amount of pressure over a long period of time . . . We are currently milking in a 'bail', which is a portable milker, and that is really hard work. The new saying is, 'It will be worth it in the long run' and I really hope we are right.

Q What motivates you to continue to 'Make Hay' even when the sun isn't always shining? Do you think working with family plays a part in this?

A Working with the family, doing a job I truly love and just enjoying life . . . I'm one of the luckiest guys in the world. I just wish I could slow down time.

ACKNOWLEDGEMENTS

My biggest thanks are to my family: Mum, Dad, Penny and Amy for your love and encouragement and making me the man I am today.

To my wonderful wife, Jo, for always being my biggest cheerleader and for your never-ending support... especially when I'm working late into the night or falling asleep by your side!

A huge shout-out to Nathan Joyce for working on this book with me, your help made this all possible and I'm grateful for the chats and your dedication to the project.

To my United Agents team Jamie, Zoe and Olivia, thanks for believing there was a book in me and finding me a publisher to work with.

At Octopus I would like to thank my editor, Briony Gowlett, for her reassurance and for making this project happen. I apologise for the delayed deadlines! Sybella Stephens for her work on the text and Yasia Williams, Peter Adlington and Chris Terry for the cover. Thanks too to Matt Grindon and Megan Brown for telling people the book is out there!

A huge thank you to everyone who helped with the farm build this year. To Pete Marquis for knocking it all down, and the Waring team for building it back up.

A massive thanks to our neighbour for his neverending support! Tom Gallagher and the river team!

There are many more people to thank – you know who you are! – and I'm glad you'll meet them with every page of the book turned.

And of course, to all the girls on the farm, by which of course I mean Tilly and her mates… couldn't do it without you girls!

ABOUT THE AUTHOR

TOM PEMBERTON is a beef and dairy farmer based on the Fylde coast in Lytham St Annes, Lancashire. As well as running a popular YouTube channel Tom Pemberton Farm Life, he works full time on the family farm. He has previously won Digital Innovator of the Year at the British Farming awards. This is his first book.